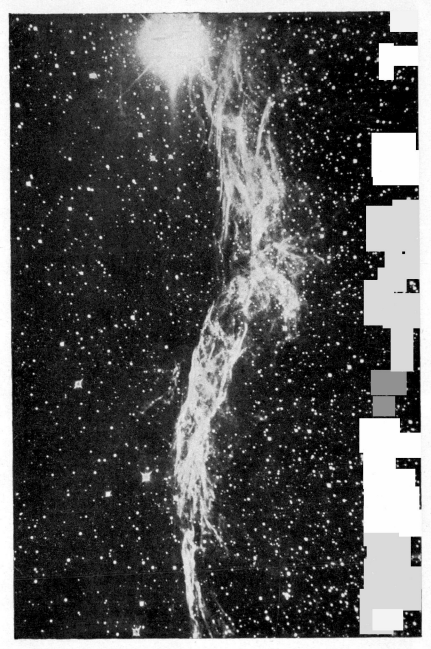

FILAMENTOUS NEBULA IN CYGNUS

At the top of the photograph there is a bright round patch with four
diffraction rays. This is the star κ Cygni. Stars on one side of the nebula
seem to be much more numerous than on the other but it is very probable
that this is appearance only. It is believed that the nebula forms the
bright illuminated edge of a dark cloud of absorbing matter which conceals
the fainter stars from our view.

FROM
ATOMS TO STARS

by

MARTIN DAVIDSON, D.Sc., F.R.A.S.

HUTCHINSON'S
SCIENTIFIC & TECHNICAL PUBLICATIONS
LONDON : NEW YORK : MELBOURNE : SYDNEY

First Edition, December 1944.
Second Edition, March 1946

THE TYPOGRAPHY (AND BINDING)
OF THIS BOOK CONFORMS TO THE
AUTHORIZED ECONOMY STANDARDS.

Made and Printed in Great Britain at St. Albans by *The
Mayflower Press (of Plymouth)*. William Brendon & Son, Ltd.
1946

PREFACE

THIS BOOK IS INTENDED TO PROVIDE A GENERAL OUTLINE OF THE MOST up-to-date knowledge of the heavenly bodies and also to show the methods employed by the astronomer to derive their distances, sizes, masses, temperatures, etc. The mathematics and physics required for this purpose are elementary—about the standard attained by those leaving school. Numerous examples specially designed to illustrate points arising in the text have been inserted, and as these are worked out fully, readers should have no difficulty in following the methods of computation. The author always uses a computing machine for his calculations, but if readers are not similarly equipped the results can be checked by a slide rule or logarithms.

The subject of atomic physics is briefly dealt with in Chapter I, but this branch is not specially required until we come to deal with the source of stellar radiation in Chapters XI and XII. These last two chapters cannot be read intelligently until Chapter I is thoroughly understood, but if the reader prefers, he can omit Chapter I at first and proceed to the descriptive portions of the book. In some cases where a mathematical treatment of a problem may be outside the standard of the reader it has been relegated to an Appendix, but there is no necessity to trouble with this part if it is too advanced, as the book can be understood without studying the Appendices.

Instead of giving details of each planet separately a number of data have been collected in tabular form at the end of Chapter VI, and it is hoped that this arrangement will prove more convenient than a detailed description in each case. Those who desire a ready description of the planets can turn to these tables for reference ; the methods by which the data have been derived are explained in the preceding chapter.

It is hoped that the outline provided in this book will stimulate readers to pursue the subject in more advanced works, a list of which is given at the end of this book, and also at the end of a few chapters.

I am grateful to the publishers for many of the illustrations reproduced from their large book *The Splendour of the Heavens* (at present out of print) and also to Mr. W. H. Johnson who suggested this book and has been most helpful both in its writing and in seeing it through the press.

MARTIN DAVIDSON.

1944, *October*.

PREFACE TO SECOND EDITION

IN THE PREPARATION OF THE SECOND EDITION I HAVE TAKEN ADVANTAGE of several suggestions made by reviewers and correspondents, to whom I am very grateful. A few misprints have been corrected and the lower diagram on p. 87, which was upside down in the first edition, has been rectified.

M. DAVIDSON.

1945, July.

CONTENTS

THE SOLAR SYSTEM

READERS WILL FIND IT EASIER TO UNDERSTAND CHAPTER I, WHICH describes the structure of the atom, if Chapter III is anticipated and a very brief account of the solar system is outlined.

For a long time people believed that the planets moved in circles, and this belief delayed important scientific discoveries. Even when Copernicus set forth his views in 1543 regarding the motions of the planets round the sun, he assumed that 'the motions of the heavenly bodies are uniform, circular, uninterrupted, or are made up of combined circular motions.' It was not until 1609 that Kepler announced two of his three famous laws of planetary motion, the first of which stated that each of the planets moved round the sun in an *elliptical* orbit. Before the time of Kepler, whatever scheme had been adopted to explain the motions of the heavenly bodies, it had been assumed that the orbits were *circular* because the circle was the 'perfect curve.' A simple if somewhat crude example of an ellipse can be obtained by the following piece of apparatus.

Take a piece of wire and bend it into a circular form. Then squash in the wire a little at two places diametrically opposite, and the resulting shape will give an idea of an ellipse. A more detailed description of this curve is given in Appendix I, which readers who desire fuller information on the subject can consult.

It is a remarkable fact that the ultra-microscopic particles composing the atom—also ultra-microscopic—should move in orbits like those described by the planets round the sun. The nucleus of the atom acts like the sun, and the small units of negative electricity, known as the electrons, are like the planets in so far as they describe ellipses (or circles) round the nucleus. A circle is a possible curve for a planet, though no planet or any other heavenly body, so far as is known, moves in an exact circle. The orbit of the planet Venus approaches a circle more closely than does the orbit of any other planet, and if you drew the orbit of Venus on a very large scale you would find it difficult to distinguish it from a circle. Just as a circle is a possible curve for a planet so it is a possible curve for an electron, but the number of cases in which a circle is found in the orbits of electrons is small.

The sun *appears* to move round the earth in a year, this apparent motion being due to the earth's orbital motion round the sun. The *apparent* orbit of the sun, relative to the earth, lies in a plane which is known as the *plane of the ecliptic*. No doubt if there were inhabitants on other planets, they would adopt their own plane of the ecliptic, which would not be the same as ours, though that of Mars would differ from ours by less than 2°, and those for Neptune, Jupiter and Uranus would show even smaller deviations than that for Mars. With the exception of Pluto, the orbits of all the planets lie nearly in the same plane, but this does not apply to the small planets known as the *asteroids* or *minor planets*, of which about 2,000 have been discovered already, and more are found

every year.   Some of them move in orbits which have fairly high inclinations, and also some move in comparatively close to, and at other times
they are far away from, the sun.

Law of Attraction

The sun attracts all the bodies revolving round him, and the attractive
force between the sun and any planet varies directly as the product of
their masses, and inversely as the square of the distance between them.
This can be illustrated by the following simple example.

The mean distance of Venus from the sun is 0·723 times the mean
distance of the earth, and the mass of Venus is 0·826 that of the earth.
Compare the attraction of the sun on Venus with his attraction on the
earth.

There is no necessity to know either the absolute mass of any of the
bodies under consideration or the absolute distance of each planet from
the sun, because we are only determining the *relative* attractions.   If
M_s, M_v, M_e, are the masses of the sun, Venus and the earth, respectively,
and D_v, D_e are the distances of Venus and the earth from the sun, the law
states that the attractions of the sun for Venus and the earth are $M_s M_v/D_v^2$
and $M_s M_e/D_e^2$, so that the ratio is simply M_v/D_v^2 divided by M_e/D_e^2. Taking
M_e and D_e as units of our mass and distance, M_v and D_v are 0·826 and
0·723, so that the ratio required is simply 0·826/(0·723)², or 1·58.

We see then that, though Venus is less massive than the earth, the
attraction of the sun on the planet is more than half as much again as
it is on the earth.   The reason is because Venus is closer to the sun than
the earth is, and, if we could imagine a comparatively small planet very
close to the sun, the attraction on it might be enormous in comparison
with that on much heavier planets far away from the sun.

Not only does the sun attract the planets ; each planet attracts
every other planet and disturbs very slightly their motions round the sun.
If two planets came close together this disturbance would be very great,
but there are never very close approaches between the planets and so
the perturbation (the name given to the disturbance caused by the
attraction of one body on another) of even the largest planet on the
smallest planet is small.   This does not apply to the asteroids, some of
which move near a few of the larger planets and are pulled out of their
orbits to a certain extent, but we need not consider these at present.

It should be noticed that the force between the sun and planets or
between one planet and another is *attractive*, not *repulsive*.   It may also
be pointed out that the sun—the central body of the solar system—
weighs about 745 times as much as all the planets combined.

CHAPTER I

STRUCTURE OF THE ATOM

The Atom a Solar System

IN THE INTRODUCTION WE SAW THAT THE SOLAR SYSTEM CONSISTED OF
a massive central body whose attractive force was responsible for the
revolution of a number of smaller and less massive bodies, called the

planets, round the central body.   Now imagine a miniature solar system in which the planets are replaced by negative charges of electricity, called *electrons*, and in which the sun is replaced by a *nucleus* which is very much heavier than an electron, and that this nucleus carries with it one or more charges of positive electricity.   Imagine, further, that the electrons which are revolving round the nucleus do not lie even approximately in one plane, as the planets do, and this will give a good picture of the atom. Something will be said about the dimensions and masses of these electrons and nuclei, but, as this is not a work on physics, descriptions of the methods adopted for measuring these quantities are beyond our scope. The reader must be prepared to accept the results which are given and, if further information is required, to consult text-books on atomic physics.

In the description of very small lengths the system in general use will be adopted for the sake of convenience.   Instead of describing a length or any other dimension as one-tenth, one-hundredth, etc., 10 raised to a negative power will be used.   Thus, 10^{-1}, 10^{-2}, 10^{-6} denote one-tenth, one-hundredth, one-millionth, and so on.   As the centimetre and gramme will be used for measuring length and mass, some idea of their English equivalents is essential for those who have not been accustomed to think in the decimal system.   The following approximate values will suffice for our purpose :

One centimetre is 0·4 inch.

One gramme is 0·0022 pound, or 0·035 ounce, or 15 grains.

An atom of hydrogen weighs about $1·5 \times 10^{-24}$ gramme and is the lightest of all atoms.   The weights of other atoms can be found by multiplying the weight of the hydrogen atom by the atomic weight of the element.   Thus, the atom of gold weighs 196 times as much as the hydrogen atom, or nearly 3×10^{-22} grammes.   (The atomic weight of gold is 196.)

The electron weighs about 1/1850 as much as the hydrogen atom, so that the weight of the electron is only 8×10^{-28} gramme.   It will be seen from this that the relation between the weight of an atom and that of an electron is comparable with the relation between the weight of the sun and one of the larger planets.   In fact, the sun weighs more than a thousand times as much as Jupiter, the heaviest of all the planets.   The nucleus of the hydrogen atom, which is called a *proton*, contains practically all the mass of the atom, and the same applies to all atoms because the mass of the electron is negligible.   A hydrogen atom—the simplest of all atoms in structure—consists of a proton and an electron revolving round it, just like the sun and one planet.   Under normal circumstances the diameter of the hydrogen atom is about 10^{-8} centimetre, and, while the sizes of the proton and electron are not known with great accuracy, they are probably about 10^{-5} the size of the whole atom.   This refers to linear dimensions, and if we wish to compare *volumes* it is necessary to raise the last dimension to the third power, so that an atom has a volume of the order 10^{15} that of an electron or proton.   Expressed in another way, we can say that the atom is about a thousand million million times the volume of an electron.

The nucleus of hydrogen—the *proton*—carries with it one unit of positive electricity, and as the electron is simply a negative charge of electricity, the hydrogen atom is normally electrically neutral, because the positive charge neutralizes the negative charge.   If the atom should

lose its electron, it becomes positively electrified, and it is important to notice that an atom receives a positive charge by *losing* an electron. The loss of an electron makes no practical difference to the mass of the atom because, as we have seen, nearly all the mass resides in the proton.

Different Orbits of the Electron

The electron can move in any one of a fixed number of orbits at various distances from the nucleus, and these orbits can be circular or elliptical. When the atom is not disturbed, the electron moves in the orbit at the least possible distance from the nucleus, which, as we have seen, is about $0 \cdot 5 \times 10^{-8}$ centimetres. Its orbital velocity is much greater than anything that we ever experience, with the exception of light, and in fact it

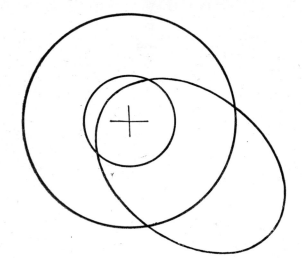

Fig. 1. The electron can revolve in a certain number of different orbits round the nucleus marked +, which is in the focus of the various ellipses described. The orbits can also be circles.

is about $0 \cdot 0075$ the velocity of light. We know that light travels 300,000 kilometres a second, so that the electron has an orbital velocity of 2,200 kilometres a second or 22×10^7 centimetres a second. A simple calculation shows that the circumference of its orbit is about 3×10^{-8} centimetres and that it takes 14×10^{-17} second to complete a revolution, or in other words, it makes about seven thousand million million revolutions each second. Fig. 1 shows some of the orbits in which the electron of a hydrogen atom can revolve round the nucleus +.

When we come to deal with atoms other than those of hydrogen, certain complications arise. First of all, there is more than one electron to consider, and these may not move in the same plane. Then the electrons exercise a *repulsive* effect on one another because bodies with like charges of electricity repel one another, bodies with unlike charges attracting one another. While the electrons are all attracted by the nucleus in accordance with the inverse square law, as in the case of the planets and the sun, they also perturb one another, as the planets do,

only relatively more so. It must be borne in mind that the nucleus *in itself* does not attract the electrons ; it is the positive electricity carried by the nucleus that attracts them, and the forces between electrons and the nucleus are not very much different from those between the electrons at the same distances. For this reason, the perturbations between electrons revolving round the nucleus are enormous in comparison with those that occur in the case of the planets.

It will be simpler if we consider the distribution of the electrons in the atoms of the elements with low atomic weights, and the next element after hydrogen in the periodic series* is helium with atomic weight 4. In its normal unelectrified state the helium atom has two electrons, and so that these should be neutralized the nucleus has twice as much positive electricity as has the hydrogen nucleus. The third element, lithium, with atomic weight 7, has three electrons and three units of positive electricity in its nucleus. Beryllium, the fourth in the series, with atomic weight 9, has four electrons and the same number of positive charges attached to the nucleus, and so on. Uranium comes ninety-second on the list and, as might be expected, has ninety-two electrons revolving round the nucleus which, in turn, must have the same number of positive units to render the atom electrically neutral. Notice that the atomic weight of an element denotes the mass of its nucleus, that of hydrogen being the unit.

Rings of Electrons

It is believed that the electrons are arranged around the nucleus, marked + in the diagrams, in rings or shells but not in a haphazard manner. There are certain stable configurations of the electronic shells and these are seen in Fig. 2, where two electrons are shown in the first stable shell, eight in the next two, and eighteen in others, but certain complications arise in these latter, and for the present only the action between atoms with three shells will be considered.

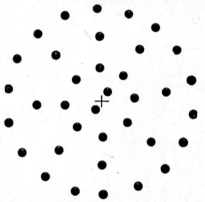

Take the case of sodium, which comes eleventh in the periodic series, and which will, therefore, have eleven electrons. The stable arrangement would be two in the first shell, eight in the second, and then eight in the third or none there, but as there are eleven electrons, the third shell can contain one only. Now this arrangement is not stable and like an object balanced on a small surface with the centre of gravity very high, a very small disturbance will upset

Fig. 2. The electrons of atoms other than hydrogen are arranged in shells around the nucleus. Stable configurations consist of 2, 8, 8 and 18 electrons in the shells. The chemical and physical properties of atoms are due to the number of electrons in their outer shells.

equilibrium. Hence the sodium atom is not stable and we shall now see, by referring to Fig. 3, what will readily disturb its stability.

* The number of an element in the periodic series is the same as the number of electrons that its atom contains.

Chlorine is seventeenth on the periodic series and hence has seventeen electrons. The first ring has two and the second has eight electrons, but how are the remaining seven to be arranged ? We have seen that the third ring should contain eight electrons to produce stability, but only seven are available. Now suppose the atom of chlorine approaches the atom of sodium, what will occur ? A condition exists where mutual assistance is urgently demanded—the sodium atom possessing an electron in its third ring which it is anxious to get rid of because it is rendering the atom unstable, and the chlorine atom possessing seven electrons also in its third ring, which are clamouring for another electron to make the ring stable. The result of the approach is that the sodium atom will lose an electron and become positively charged in doing so, while the chlorine atom will acquire an electron and become negatively charged.

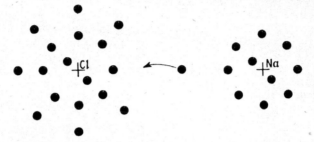

Fig. 3. The outer shell of the chlorine atom has 7 electrons and hence is unstable. The outer shell of the sodium atom has only one electron and is also unstable. When the chlorine atom annexes the outer electron of the sodium atom, equilibrium is restored in both atoms and a molecule of sodium chloride is formed

The forces of electric attraction will make the two atoms hold together, forming a molecule of sodium chloride, or our ordinary table-salt.

One other example will be taken to show how more than one atom of one element can enter into chemical combination with one atom of another, to form a molecule.

Oxygen, the eighth in the series, has eight electrons, the first ring containing two and the second ring six. Two additional electrons are required with the second ring to make it stable, and let us examine the reaction when a hydrogen atom approaches an oxygen atom. The second ring requires two electrons to complete the work of producing stability and hence one atom of hydrogen, containing only one electron, will not be able to satisfy the need. If, however, two atoms of hydrogen approach the oxygen atom, the outer shell of the latter will eagerly seize the two electrons to complete its stability, and a molecule of water, H_2O, will be the result. Many other examples could be given, but these will suffice to illustrate the explanation of chemical reactions on the theory of electronic shells. It will be seen that the outer shells are responsible for the reactions that occur when chemical combination takes place.

One other point is worth noticing. What will happen if two atoms approach each other, each atom requiring one or more electrons to complete the outer ring, or each atom possessing superfluous electrons which it would gladly discard to produce equilibrium ? This question is easily answered by examining the atoms of oxygen and chlorine (Fig.

4), the former requiring two electrons and the latter one electron to complete the outer rings. Obviously there will be no tendency to combine because each requires what the other is unable to supply. Similarly,

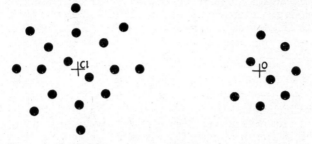

Fig. 4. The outer shell of the oxygen atom has 6 electrons and requires 2 more to complete the shell. The outer shell of the chlorine atom requires one clectron to complete it. As neither shell can supply what the other requires, there is little chemical affinity between the atoms.

in the case of sodium which has an electron in its third ring that it wants to get rid of, and a hydrogen atom which has only one electron and is also anxious to get rid of it. The result, again, is that neither atom is able to satisfy the needs of the other, and there will be no chemical action.

The Atomic Nucleus

Up to the present very little has been said about the nucleus of the atom. We have seen that the nucleus of the hydrogen atom consists of the simple unit known as a proton, and outside this an electron is revolving in orbits which may be various circles or ellipses. When we come to deal with atoms other than hydrogen the number of protons increases, and in the normal state there must be just as many electrons as there are positive charges with the protons. The atomic nucleus will be better understood from a consideration of radio-activity.

Radio-Activity

Although radio-activity is usually associated with radium, Monsieur and Madame Curie discovered radium when they were working under the directions of Becquerel, who first discovered radio-activity from uranium emanations. They noticed that pitchblende, from which uranium is obtained, was actually more radio-active than uranium itself. Their search for a more radio-active substance than uranium led to the discovery of radium. The rapidity of disintegration is measured by the time required for half a given collection of atoms of any radio-active substance to disintegrate, and it has been found that there is a very great difference in this time with different substances. Uranium requires 45×10^8 years, and the first product of disintegration is a substance which requires 24 days, this again breaking down into another substance whose period is less than a minute and a quarter. The next substance has a period of about two million years, and at this stage two different products may be formed, one of which becomes radium with a period of 1580 years, the other becoming proto-actinium, the period of which is

12,000 years, actinium being the next product. Radium produces the inert gas niton or radon, sometimes referred to as the radium emanation, for which the period is a little less than four days. The end of the series is a form of lead which is not radio-active. It must be remembered that all the periods given refer to the time required for *half* of a given collection of atoms to disintegrate.

Emanations from Radio-Active Substances

Radio-active substances emit one or more of three kinds of rays of which two are important for our present purpose. There are first of all the α-rays which have been found to consist of particles, each of which is the nucleus of a helium atom, and therefore possesses a mass four times that of the hydrogen atom. They have a positive charge double that of the hydrogen nucleus, which, as we have seen, carries only one unit of positive electricity. Because they have this double positive charge they attract electrons as they are shot out from radio-active substances with a high velocity—sometimes as much as one-tenth that of light. By removing electrons from atoms which they meet, they become ordinary helium atoms, electrically neutral, but they leave the atoms from which

Fig. 5.   Radium breaks down spontaneously into radon and helium, an example of the transmutation of one element into another.

they have removed the electrons positively electrified. Two things take place with the substance which shoots out these α-rays. First of all, as they are nuclei of helium which has atomic weight 4, the atomic weight of the substance decreases by 4. Then, as the nucleus of the atom loses two units of positive electricity, the atom must move down two places in the periodic series. Thus, radium with atomic weight 226 and atomic number 88, sends out α-particles and becomes radon with atomic weight 222 and atomic number 86 (see Fig. 5). The medieval alchemists were not far wrong when they dreamt of the artificial transmutation of one element into another.

Radio-active substances also emit β-rays which are simply electrons. (The γ-rays emitted in addition to the α- and β-rays are not particles but are of the nature of light-waves, and we are not specially concerned with them in nuclear transformations.) The β-rays move with very high velocities—in some cases 99 per cent that of light. (For reasons given in works on relativity, it is impossible for anything material to attain the velocity of light.) As radio-activity gives rise to new elements, and an element depends upon its nucleus, both α- and β-particles must emanate from the nucleus.

Up to the present we have not said much about the nature of the nucleus, but have referred to the charge or charges of positive electricity that it carries. These charges are not the nucleus but are associated with it. It appears, therefore, that the nucleus contains both α-particles

and electrons. This provides us with a better view of the atom, including the nucleus, than was given previously, but, as we shall see, electrons probably do not actually *exist* inside the nucleus.

In some respects it seems reasonable to expect that the nucleus of an atom contains electrons, as otherwise there would be nothing to hold together a collection of protons which would repel one another owing to their positive charges. The introduction of electrons amongst them would serve to keep them together because of the attraction between the negative and positive charges. Some have compared the electrons to a kind of cement which holds the protons together, but there is still a considerable amount of speculation on the structure of the atomic nucleus, and physicists have reasons to believe that electrons do not actually exist inside the nucleus. This does not contradict the view that they are sometimes expelled by radio-active substances. It is thought that they are 'created,' just before their emission, out of 'shapeless' electric charges carried by the nucleus. A useful analogy can be found in the case of soap-bubbles which do not exist as bubbles inside a pipe before they are blown, but exist and are visible when they are blown out of the pipe. A more satisfactory view of the nucleus is given on page 19, and this picture is generally adopted now.

Bombardment of Atoms by α-particles

Some elements, when subjected to an intense bombardment by α-particles, have been found to give off hydrogen. The bombardment must be intense because, on the law of probability, comparatively few of the α-particles will make a head-on collision with a nucleus, which occupies an extremely small portion of the total volume of an atom. A direct collision is necessary ; it will not suffice if the α-particles merely pass close to the nucleus. The result of carrying out this bombardment on nitrogen atoms is interesting.

Blackett, one of Rutherford's students, bombarded ordinary air, which consists largely of nitrogen, in a *Wilson's Cloud Chamber*, and photographed the result. A Wilson Cloud Chamber is described at the end of the chapter, and it will be sufficient now to say something about the results of the bombardment and the photographs that were taken.

After Blackett had taken 23,000 photographs he found that eight of these showed head-on collisions of α-particles with the nuclei of nitrogen atoms. As a result of the impact on a nucleus it was found that a proton, that is, a hydrogen nucleus, had been ejected from the interior of the nitrogen nucleus and the α-particle had completely disappeared, or rather, the track which the α-particle left had disappeared. It is obvious that the α-particle had stuck to the nucleus of the nitrogen atom at the time of the collision, and the nucleus was no longer a nucleus of nitrogen but something different. In fact, to the original nitrogen nucleus there had been added a nucleus of helium, which is an α-particle, but a nucleus of hydrogen, which is a proton, had been knocked out of the nucleus. The result of the operation can be shown as follows :

Original nitrogen nucleus, atomic number 7, atomic weight 14
Add a helium   ,,   ,,   ,, 2   ,,   ,,   4
Deduct a hydrogen   ,,   ,,   ,, 1   ,,   ,,   1
Final result is a   ,,   ,,   ,, 8   ,,   ,,   17

B

Now we know that the atomic number 8 corresponds to the oxygen atom and also that the atomic weight 17 represents the heavy isotope of oxygen, so the result of the bombardment by the α-particles is to transmute the atom of nitrogen into an atom of oxygen, a hydrogen nucleus being set free. (See Fig. 6.)

It is necessary to say something about isotopes which play a very important part in many chemical reactions. The word *isotope* means occupying the same place, and the word is applied to those atoms that are identical in their number of electrons and in chemical and physical properties, but differ in mass. Suppose we could introduce into the nucleus of an atom, say of chlorine, an additional pair of one electron and one proton. The net charge would remain the same, because the positive electricity associated with the proton would be neutralized by the electron. From what has been said earlier, the number of electrons in the rings would remain unchanged, and as the outer electrons determine the chemical reactions, these latter would remain practically unaltered. The addition of one proton would increase the atomic weight by 1 unit

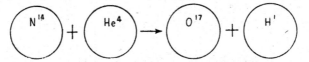

Fig. 6. When the nucleus of a nitrogen atom is struck by an α-particle (a helium atom), a hydrogen nucleus is set free and an atom of the heavy isotope of oxygen is formed.

(the extra electron would add a mass of only 1/1,850 that of a proton, and this can be ignored), and hence we should have two atoms with almost the same properties but with different atomic weight.

It is now known that ordinary chlorine is a mixture of two kinds of atoms and that 75 per cent consist of atoms with mass 35, the mass of the hydrogen atom being the unit, the other 25 per cent consisting of atoms with mass 37. If we wish to find the average atomic weight of the mixture we proceed thus :

$(75 \times 35 + 25 \times 37)/100 = 35 \cdot 5$, which is therefore the weight required.

The actual atomic weight of chlorine is given as $35 \cdot 46$, and the agreement is as good as can be expected.

The existence of isotopes explains why there are many other elements like chlorine whose atomic weights are not an exact whole number. If atoms are built up from protons, a proton being the mass of a hydrogen atom, we should expect that atomic weights would always be whole numbers or very nearly so. In point of fact, atomic weights are practically whole numbers, but sometimes there is a mixture of elements which have the same chemical and physical characteristics, owing to the same number of electrons, but which differ in atomic weight, because of the presence of one or more extra protons in the nucleus. Obviously the atomic weight of the mixture, which is classified as *one* element, will not necessarily be a whole number.

Oxygen is another instance of an isotope. In atmospheric air there is $99 \cdot 97$ per cent of oxygen with atomic weight 16 and $0 \cdot 03$ per cent with

atomic weight 17. The average atomic weight of the mixture is easily seen to be 16·0003. Atmospheric nitrogen is also an isotope, 99·7 per cent having atomic weight 14 and 0·3 per cent having atomic weight 15, the average atomic weight of the mixture being 14·003.

Up to the present we have spoken of two elementary particles, the protons and the electrons, but within the last twelve years other elementary particles have been discovered which assist considerably in explaining more clearly the structure of the nucleus of an atom.

In 1932, while Chadwick was experimenting on atomic disintegration, he discovered particles with nearly the same mass as the hydrogen atom but they were *uncharged*. These particles, to which the name *neutrons* was given (to denote that they were electrically neutral), are about the

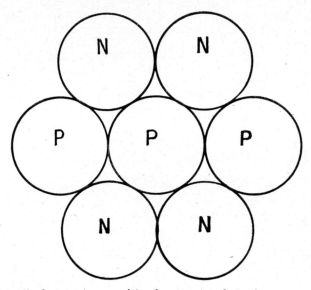

Fig. 7. A hydrogen atom consists of one proton, but other atoms consist of protons and neutrons, a neutron having the mass of a proton, but carrying no electric charge. The protons and neutrons are packed very closely together.

same size and mass as a proton. Later, another important discovery was made by Anderson, an American physicist, while he was investigating the property of cosmic rays (radiation from the depths of space with a very high power of penetration). He discovered new particles to which the name *positron* was given. They are of the same weight as the electrons, but instead of having a negative elementary charge, they have a *positive* elementary charge. It is remarkable that Dirac had predicted the existence of these particles many years before Anderson's discovery, his prediction being based on theoretical considerations.

The importance of the discovery of the neutron in simplifying our conception of the structure of the nucleus will be obvious from an inspection of Fig. 7. Consider a nucleus of mass 7 units and charge 3 units. Clearly it may be considered to be composed of 3 protons and 4 neutrons. This nucleus is a constituent of lithium, atomic weight 7 and atomic

number 3. The number of electrons revolving round the nucleus is not altered by the discovery, and all that has been said previously about these electrons still holds. The behaviour of neutrons seems extraordinary at first, but when it is remembered that they are not electrically charged there is nothing strange about their movements. While a proton is stopped by a sheet of lead a fraction of a millimetre thick, a neutron moving with the same velocity can penetrate sheets of lead as much as 20 centimetres in thickness. The reason is that the proton with its charge of electricity annexes the electrons of atoms which lie in its path (the atom which loses an electron is said to be ionized, and if two electrons are lost it is doubly ionized, and so on), and it is inevitable that some of the energy of motion of the proton is lost each time an electron is attracted and annexed. Hence the proton is brought to rest in a very short space. Now look at the motion of a neutron with the same velocity. As it does not possess a charge either positive or negative, it will neither attract nor repel the electrons of any atoms which lie in its path, but will pass through the skeleton of the atom without losing velocity. A collision with the *nucleus* of an atom is, however, absolutely certain at some stage of its journey, though such a collision is relatively a rare event. For this reason a neutron can penetrate a great thickness of matter without colliding with any nucleus. (See Fig. 8.)

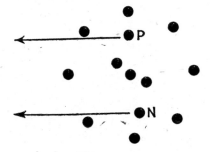

Fig. 8. A proton, marked P, exerts a positive charge of electricity and hence attracts the electrons in an atom, just as one planet attracts another. Hence there is a greater probability that P will collide with an electron than there is that the neutron N will collide, because N does not attract the electrons to itself. This explains the high penetrating power of neutrons.

The discovery of the neutron has afforded a simple explanation of the heavy isotope of hydrogen, known as *deuterium*. It has been found that water containing this isotope is about 5 per cent heavier than ordinary water and would be very advantageous to indifferent swimmers. This heavy hydrogen nucleus is made up of one proton and one neutron, the complete atom consisting of this nucleus and a revolving electron. In fact, the heavy hydrogen nucleus was split up by means of the very short-wave γ-radiation, the deuterium being resolved into a proton and a neutron. The heavy hydrogen atom is sometimes known as the *deuteron*.

We have seen that bombardment by α-particles transformed nitrogen into oxygen, and a number of similar transmutations of one element into another have been effected in the same way, such as sodium into magnesium, boron into carbon, and aluminium into silicon, but as such transformations become more difficult with increasing atomic weight of the element, a limit is finally reached, and beyond argon no disintegration has been observed through α-particles bombardment.

Bombardment by Protons

It has been found that greater efficiency can be obtained by using protons for the bombardment of the nuclei of atoms. A beam of these

particles is produced by accelerating hydrogen ions (an ion of hydrogen is a hydrogen atom which carries a single positive charge) in an intense electric field, and very high velocities can be obtained in this way. Some of the reactions are shown in Fig. 9, and the transformation of nitrogen into the light isotope of carbon is of special importance. Some reference will be made to this later. Cockcroft and Walton, two of Rutherford's pupils, were the pioneers in using swift-flying protons to disintegrate the atom, and now there are several laboratories in various parts of the world with an apparatus to break up the atom, not only of the lighter elements, but of the heavier elements as well. A description of the apparatus known as a *cyclotron* is beyond our present scope, and readers must refer to works on atomic physics for a full account of this interesting subject. Lawrence's method for splitting the atom is extremely effective, employing not only protons but also deuterons and helium ions, and this nuclear artillery has resulted in breaking up the atom on a scale previously

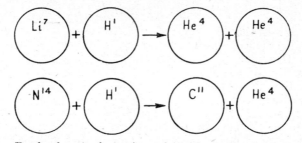

Fig. 9. Bombardment of atomic nuclei with protons has proved very effective, and the result is shown in the case of lithium and nitrogen. In the former case two helium atoms are produced, and in the latter case the light isotope of carbon and helium result from the bombardment.

undreamt-of. From what has just been said about the penetrative power of neutrons, the reader might surmise that these particles could become dangerous to human life, and he would be correct in this conjecture. It has been found necessary to set up thick barricades against the neutrons and also to keep the experimenters as far as possible from the source of danger.

Nuclear Energy

It has been found that the diameters of all atomic nuclei lie within the limits 10^{-12} cm., which is the diameter of the hydrogen nucleus, and about 2×10^{-12} cm. for the heaviest nuclei. As the heaviest nuclei contain more than 200 particles altogether, these must be packed very tightly. An estimate of this tight packing shows that if we could take a handful of nuclei, packed together like the protons and neutrons in the nuclei, it would weigh about 100 million tons. The amount of energy released by nuclear reactions is obviously enormous, and if only some method of harnessing it could be devised many of our industrial and economic problems might be solved. An example will show how much energy is released when an atom is split.

It has been found that when a proton collides with a lithium atom and splits it up into two helium atoms, $2 \cdot 8 \times 10^{-5}$ ergs of energy are liberated. This may seem very small, but let us examine the figures

more carefully. We have seen that the hydrogen atom weighs $1 \cdot 5 \times 10^{-24}$ grammes, and since the atomic weight of lithium is 7, a lithium atom weighs 7 times this amount, which is about 10^{-23} grammes. Hence, in one gramme of lithium there are 10^{23} atoms, so that the total energy available in this weight is $2 \cdot 8 \times 10^{-5}$ erg multiplied by 10^{23} or $2 \cdot 5 \times 10^{18}$ ergs. One horse-power is $7 \cdot 46 \times 10^{9}$ ergs per second, and therefore one gramme of lithium, weighing just over 15 grains or about 1/28th of an ounce, if disintegrated in a second, would develop 3×10^{8}, or three hundred million horse-power. It is fortunate for the continuation of our existence on this planet that atomic disintegration is an extremely slow process, as otherwise the energy liberated would be destructive to all forms of life. Although slow-scale transformations are all that can be accomplished at present by artificial methods, we shall see that under the conditions of high temperature prevailing in the interior of our sun and other stars, large-scale transformations are continuously in process.

Matter and Energy

We have seen that the nuclei of different elements may be regarded as being collections of an integral number of hydrogen nuclei or protons, together with neutrons. A curious anomaly was brought to light when it was discovered that the mass of the hydrogen atom itself did not conform to the rule, its mass being $1 \cdot 008$ if the atom of oxygen is taken as 16. This discrepancy has been explained on the electro-magnetic theory of mass. On the Principle of Relativity all mass, whether electrical in its origin or not, should increase with increasing velocity, and on this principle the electrical mass of a number of small charged particles diminishes when the particles are crowded into a very small space. If we regard the nucleus of helium as consisting of four protons packed in a small volume, we should expect, from what has just been said, that the mass of the helium atom should be a little less than four times that of the hydrogen atom. The name *packing effect* is applied to the loss of mass which takes place.

Under certain conditions matter and energy are mutually convertible, and the energy which accompanies the loss of mass m is mc^2, where c is the velocity of light. Now consider the loss of mass when four protons each of mass $1 \cdot 008$, are packed together to form a helium atom. This is obviously $(4 \times 0 \cdot 008) \times (1 \cdot 5 \times 10^{-24})$ gm., since, as we saw, a proton weighs about $1 \cdot 5 \times 10^{-24}$ gm. This amounts to about 5×10^{-26} gm., and the evolution of energy should be $(5 \times 10^{-26}) \times (9 \times 10^{20})$ ergs, since the velocity of light is 3×10^{10} cms. per second. Hence the condensation of four hydrogen atoms to form an atom of helium evolves 45×10^{-6} ergs. The four hydrogen atoms weigh 6×10^{-24} gm., so one gramme of hydrogen, in forming helium, would evolve $7 \cdot 5 \times 10^{18}$ ergs. Thus if 1 gramme of hydrogen atoms condensed into helium in a second, it would evolve a thousand million horse-power. This evolution of energy should be noticed because we shall have occasion to refer to it later in dealing with transformations in the interior of the stars.

The Reality of Electrons, Protons, Neutrons, etc.

It should be pointed out that the description of the structure of the atom—a central nucleus with electrons revolving round it—and also of

the nucleus as consisting of protons and neutrons, may be merely a pictorial representation. Nevertheless it explains in a fairly satisfactory manner many phenomena connected with spectra and other matters. Of course this is no guarantee that the atom and nucleus have the structure assigned to them by physicists, because there may be, and probably some day there will be, a much simpler explanation. The old Ptolemaic system gave an explanation, of a kind, of the movements of the stars and planets, but it was based on an erroneous conception regarding the earth as the centre of the universe, all the heavenly bodies revolving round it. In the same way the Newtonian mechanics explained very satisfactorily the movements of the planets, assuming the law of inverse squares, but we know now that there were certain assumptions in his laws which were not absolutely correct. Einstein's Relativity Theory has simplified the Newtonian mechanics by showing that the laws of gravitation can be reduced to geometrical principles, and these geometrical principles are responsible for greater accuracy than could ever have been attained by means of Newtonian mechanics. The conception of the atom provides a means for explaining many phenomena, and until something better is substituted we may accept it. It may be pointed out, however, that Prof. John Tutin developed a theory according to which the electrons form the inner nucleus, the massive particles moving in orbits outside. (*The Atom*, Longmans, Green & Co., 1934). In spite of some alleged advantages of the theory, it has not had a favourable reception.

Questions relating to the nature of reality arise which are philosophical, but as this is not a treatise on philosophy it is outside the scope of the work to deal with them. The words of Sir James Jeans are apposite in this connection : "Our studies can never put us into contact with reality and its true meaning and nature must be for ever hidden from us." *Physics and Reality* (Cambridge University Press, 1942), p. 16.

The Wilson Chamber

The construction of the Cloud Chamber is due to C. T. R. Wilson, a meteorologist and physicist, who was therefore conversant with the conditions under which a mist is formed in the atmosphere. A mist cannot arise merely when there is a sufficient amount of moisture in the atmosphere ; it is essential that there should also be minute particles like specks of dust and the like, to form the nucleus for condensation. He discovered also that water-vapour can condense around the positive ions to which the α-particles give rise as they move rapidly through the air. We have seen that these particles tear off one or more electrons from atoms of gas that lie in their way, and the ionized atoms cause small droplets of water vapour in a chamber to condense, so that a thin band of fog marks the track of the projectiles. The cloud chamber is in the form of a cylinder within which a piston can be raised or lowered, so that the moist air can be brought to saturation point. Mist is then formed on the ionized atoms, and the streak of fog can be photographed. If the piston is lowered, thus compressing the air, the latter is warmed, and the fog streaks disappear, just as a mist will disappear before the heat of the sun.

It must be noticed that the α-particles themselves are not photographed ; it is only their *effect* which can be observed. We might com-

Column	0	1	2	3	4
Row 1		H 1 1			
2	He 2 2	Li 3 2, 1	Be 4 2, 2	B 5 2, 3	C 6 2, 4
3	Ne 10 2, 8	Na 11 2, 8, 1	Mg 12 2, 8, 2	Al 13 2, 8, 3	Si 14 2, 8, 4
4 A	A 18 2, 8, 8	K 19 2, 8, 8, 1	Ca 20 2, 8, 8, 2	Sc 21 2, 8, 9, 2	Ti 22 2, 8, 10, 2
4 B		Cu 29 2, 8, 18, 1	Zn 30 2, 8, 18, 2	Ga 31 2, 8, 18, 3	Ge 32 2, 8, 18, 4
5 A	Kr 36 2, 8, 18, 8	Rb 37 2, 8, 18, 8, 1	Sr 38 2, 8, 18, 8, 2	Y 39 2, 8, 18, 9, 2	Zr 40 2, 8 18, 10, 2
5 B		Ag 47 2, 8, 18, 18, 1	Cd 48 2, 8, 18, 18, 2	In 49 2, 8, 18, 18, 3	Sn 50 2, 8, 18, 18, 4
6 A	Xe 54 2, 8, 18, 18, 8	Cs 55 2, 8, 18, 18, 8, 1	Ba 56 2, 8, 18, 18, 8, 2	La to Lu 57–71	Hf 72 2, 8, 18, 32 10, 2
6 B		Au 79 2, 8, 18, 32, 18, 1	Hg 80 2, 8, 18, 32, 18, 2	Tl 81 2, 8, 18, 32, 18, 3	Pb 82 2, 8, 18, 32 18, 4
7 A	Rn 86 2, 8, 18, 32, 18, 8		Ra 88 2, 8, 18, 32, 18, 8, 2	Ac 89 2, 8, 18, 32, 18, 9, 2	Th 90 2, 8, 18, 32 18, 10, 2

5	6	7	8		
N 7 2, 5	O 8 2, 6	F 9 2, 7			
P 15 2, 8, 5	S 16 2, 8, 6	Cl 17 2, 8, 7			
V 23 8, 11, 2	Cr 24 2, 8, 13, 1	Mn 25 2, 8, 13, 2	Fe 26 2, 8, 14, 2	Co 27 2, 8, 15, 2	Ni 28 2, 8, 16, 2
As 33 8, 18, 5	Se 34 2, 8, 18, 6	Br 35 2, 8, 18, 7			
Nb 41 8, 18, 12, 1	Mo 42 2, 8, 18, 13, 1	Ma 43 2, 8, 18, 14, 1	Ru 44 2, 8, 18, 15, 1	Rh 45 2, 8, 18, 16, 1	Pd 46 2, 8, 18, 18
Sb 51 8, 18, 18, 5	Te 52 2, 8, 18, 18, 6	I 53 2, 8, 18, 18, 7			
Ta 73 8, 18, 32, 11, 2	W 74 2, 8, 18, 32, 12, 2	Re 75 2, 8, 18, 32, 13, 2	Os 76 2, 8, 18, 32, 14, 2	Ir 77 2, 8, 18, 32, 15, 2	Pt 78 2, 8, 18, 32, 16, 2
Bi 83 8, 18, 32, 18, 5	Po 84 2, 8, 18, 32, 18, 6				
Pa 91 8, 18, 32, 8, 11, 2	U 92 2, 8, 18, 32, 18, 12, 2				

pare the experiment to someone attempting to see bullets fired from a machine-gun. He will not be able to see them, unless they are tracer bullets, and even then he will not see the bullets themselves, but only the illumination from something which they carry. If, however, the machine-gun bullets are fired into a lake, he will see the splashes of water which they make, and even if he were quite deaf and so unable to hear the noise from the machine-gun, he might be able to infer from the splashes what was taking place.

The Periodic Classification and the Electronic Structure of the Elements

This Table is taken from *The Nature of the Atom*, by G. K. T. Conn, and is identical with that of Mendeléeff in his work on the relations between the elements. The modified form which shows the dissimilarity between 4A and 4B, etc., was first suggested by Bayley in 1882, on chemical grounds, and Bohr gave the explanation of it forty years later.

After each element the number in the same line (the atomic number) shows the number of positive charges in its nucleus, and in the lower line the distribution of the electrons is shown. The sum of the figures in the lower line, giving the number of electrons in the shells, will always be the same as the number of positive charges in the nucleus. The last figure in the lower line shows the number of electrons in the outer shell, and therefore gives an indication of the chemical and physical properties of the element.

Elements in the same column show reciprocal likenesses. Thus, lithium, sodium, potassium, rubidium and caesium, known as the alkali metals, are very much akin to one another. They have a common tendency to form positive ions, they give off one electron, and their spectra show a great similarity. It should be noticed that the elements in the same column for 4A and 4B, 5A and 5B, 6A and 6B, have little in common, but those in 4A, 5A and 6A resemble one another, as do those in 4B, 5B and 6 B.

Names and Symbols of the Elements in Order of Increasing Atomic Number

H	Hydrogen	A	Argon	Br	Bromine
He	Helium	K	Potassium	Kr	Krypton
Li	Lithium	Ca	Calcium	Rb	Rubidium
Be	Beryllium	Sc	Scandium	Sr	Strontium
B	Boron	Ti	Titanium	Y	Yttrium
C	Carbon	V	Vanadium	Zr	Zirconium
N	Nitrogen	Cr	Chromium	Nb	Niobium
O	Oxygen	Mn	Manganese	Mo	Molybdenum
F	Fluorine	Fe	Iron	Ma	Masurium
Ne	Neon	Co	Cobalt	Ru	Ruthenium
Na	Sodium	Ni	Nickel	Rh	Rhodium
Mg	Magnesium	Cu	Copper	Pd	Palladium
Al	Aluminium	Zn	Zinc	Ag	Silver
Si	Silicon	Ga	Gallium	Cd	Cadmium
P	Phosphorus	Ge	Germanium	In	Indium
S	Sulphur	As	Arsenic	Sn	Tin
Cl	Chlorine	Se	Selenium	Sb	Antimony

Te	Tellurium	Tb	Terbium	Pt	Platinum
I	Iodine	Dy	Dysprosium	Au	Gold
X	Xenon	Ho	Holmium	Hg	Mercury
Cs	Caesium	Er	Erbium	Tl	Thallium
Ba	Barium	Tm	Thulium	Pb	Lead
La	Lanthanum	Yb	Ytterbium	Bi	Bismuth
Ce	Cerium	Lu	Lutecium	Po	Polonium
Pr	Praseodymium	Hf	Hafnium	Rn	Radium Emanation
Nd	Neodymium	Ta	Tantalum	Ra	Radium
Il	Illinium	W	Tungsten	Ac	Actinium
Sm	Samarium	Re	Rhenium	Th	Thorium
Eu	Europium	Os	Osmium	Pa	Proto-actinium
Gd	Gadolinium	Ir	Iridium	U	Uranium

Readers who desire further information on the subject can consult a number of elementary treatises on Atomic Physics, amongst which the following will be found useful :

G. P. Thomson, *The Atom.*
Bertrand Russell, *The A.B.C. of Atoms.*
G. K. T. Conn, *The Nature of the Atom.*
J. A. Crowther, *Ions, Electrons, and Ionizing Radiations.*
C. Møller and Ebbe Rasmussen, *The World and the Atom.*
M. Born, *The Restless Universe.*
L. Infeld, *The World in Modern Science.*
B. C. Sanders, *Order and Chaos in the World of Atoms.*

CHAPTER II

THE SUN

The Sun in Mythology

THE SUN IS THE MOST IMPORTANT OBJECT AMONGST ALL THE HEAVENLY bodies, providing light and heat, without which life in every form would cease to exist. It is not surprising that the sun was an object of worship among many nations ; men knew that they were dependent on him for the preservation of their lives and that dire results would follow if he failed for only a short time to pour forth his light and heat on the earth. The ancients were aware that the temperature of the sun was inconceivably greater than anything that they experienced from his rays even in the hottest climate. The Greeks told how Phaëton drove the sun-chariot across the sky and saw the Great and Little Bear scorched with the sun's rays ; the Serpent coiled around the north pole, torpid and harmless, revived with rage through the growing heat ; Bootes in flight, encumbered as he was with his plough, and later the clouds on the earth beginning to smoke and the mountain tops to take fire. Then Phaëton beheld the world on fire and as a result the people of Ethiopia turned black because their blood was forced so suddenly to the surface, and the Libyan desert was dried up. The earth cracked open and light shone through the chinks into Tartarus, frightening even the king of shadows and his queen. Finally, earth appealed to Jupiter to save her from

destruction, and in response to her prayer he brandished a lightning bolt and launched it against the charioteer, striking him from his seat. With his hair on fire, Phaëton fell like a shooting star, and the great river Eridanus received him and cooled his burning frame. Such conceptions may seem more poetic than scientific, but in spite of this, it was a serious offence to belittle Apollo, the god of the sun. Anaxagoras, who was born about 500 B.C., was noted for his mathematical and astronomical knowledge, but his theories about the heavenly bodies brought him into conflict with the exponents of the popular faith. He taught that the sun was a mass of blazing metal, larger than Peloponnesus, and it is said that he even attempted to bring the phenomenon of meteoric stones within predictable events. He was arrested and charged with contravening the dogmas of religion, and was forced to retire from Athens to Lampsacus, where he died in 428 B.C.

Distance and Dimensions of the Sun

Probably very few people to-day believe with Anaxagoras that the sun is a mass of blazing metal, but many think that the sun is a mass of burning gas—a view which contains a substratum of truth but which is far from a true explanation of the heat and light emitted by the sun. It is very important to have clear conceptions of the physical conditions prevailing on the sun's surface and also in his interior. Our knowledge of the former is obtained largely by observational evidence, but as it is impossible to see into the interior of the sun, except for a very short distance when we are examining sun-spots, our knowledge of the conditions in the interior is based on the theoretical work of the physicist. When we understand something about the sun's physical constitution we can generalize with a certain amount of assurance, and assume that similar conditions are found on many of the stars, of which our sun is one, and indeed we might say, a typical star so far as size, density and temperature are concerned.

The distance of the sun from the earth varies, owing to the elliptical motion of the earth in its orbit, as explained in the Introduction, but its mean distance is just over 93 million miles. An idea of this distance, which it is difficult to visualize as we can visualize distances of 20, 50 or even a few hundreds of miles, may be gained from the following simple illustration. Suppose an aviator could fly day and night without any rest, and that his aeroplane was capable of travelling with an average speed of 3 miles a minute, that is, 180 miles an hour, he would require nearly 60 years' continuous flight to reach the sun. Light, which has a speed of 186,271 miles a second, requires more than eight minutes to travel from the sun to the earth. The result is that we never see the sun just where he is in the sky ; we see him where he was over eight minutes earlier.

The diameter of the sun is 864,000 miles, which is nearly 109 times the earth's diameter. By a well-known principle the volumes of spheres are proportional to the cubes of their diameters, and hence the volume of the sun is nearly $1\frac{1}{3}$ million times that of the earth, but the sun's mass is only 333,434 times that of the earth. How are we to explain this apparent anomaly ? There is only one explanation—that the sun is much less dense than the earth, and hence any volume of it must weigh

less than the corresponding volume of the earth. It has been found that the mean density of the sun is only 1·41 times that of water, so if we could obtain an *average* specimen of the sun we should find that it weighed less than half as much again as the same volume of water. In a later chapter, when it is shown how the size and mass of the earth are ascertained, it will be also shown how these can be used as the bases for finding the distances of the heavenly bodies and also for weighing them. Meanwhile the reader must accept these figures, and we shall now deal with another problem in connection with the sun—the determination of his surface temperature.

About Heat and Temperature

If a certain amount of heat be applied for the same time to different metals, as is well known, they will not attain the same temperature. Thus, the quantity of heat which would raise a gramme of copper through 10° C. would raise the same weight of silver through 16·7° C., and the same weight of iron through 8·4°C. The same quantity would raise a gramme of water through less than 1° C. We can express this in a different way by saying that the quantity of heat which would raise 10 grammes of copper through 1°C. would raise 16.7 grammes of silver, 8.4 grammes of iron, or about one gramme of water, through the same range of temperature. Notice that it requires a lot of heat to alter the temperature of water in comparison with that required to alter the temperature of metals by the same amount. It has been agreed to adopt as *the unit of heat, the quantity required to raise 1 gm. of water through 1°, from 14·5° C. to 15·5° C.*, and the name *calorie* is given to this unit. Although the quantity of heat required to raise water through 1° C. is nearly the same whatever the temperature of the water may be, it is not quite the same, and the range 14·5° to 15·5° has been adopted by physicists as the standard.

Experiment shows that an increase in temperature of 1° C. causes the pressure exerted by a gas confined in a vessel to increase by 1/273 of its previous pressure. If a temperature of −273° C. could be produced it may be assumed that the gas would cease to exert any pressure, or, in theory, would cease to exist, and it has been agreed to adopt −273° C. as the *absolute-zero*. Instead of describing a temperature as 15° C. it will often be necessary to describe it as 288° absolute, or 288° K., after Kelvin. The absolute temperature of a gas or any body is found by adding its temperature in degrees Centigrade to 273.

The Solar Constant

Before determining the temperature at the surface of the sun, it is necessary to measure the rate at which the rays of the sun raise a certain quantity of water or mercury or some other metal through a given range of temperature. A pyrheliometer is an instrument designed for this purpose and in principle is very simple. In 1837 Pouillet constructed a pyrheliometer which consisted of a copper vessel with a flat and blackened bottom, filled with water. The amount of solar radiation was determined by observing the change of temperature shown by the thermometer whose bulb was immersed in the vessel, first when the apparatus was in the shade, and then with the instrument directed towards the sun.

Many refinements were necessary which need not be mentioned, though one in particular should be noticed. The solar radiation is weakened by its passage through our atmosphere, and hence the rise of temperature when the instrument was directed towards the sun was not a true representation of the heat of the sun. By other methods the amount of this atmospheric absorption of the sun's rays is known and can be allowed for, so the *solar constant*, the number of calories per square centimetre per minute that falls on a surface, with its plane at right angles to the direction of the sun's rays, at the mean distance of the earth, assuming that atmospheric absorption has been eliminated, has been found with great accuracy. Various improvements have been made on the original apparatus and more modern instruments have been devised which enable the solar constant to be determined with greater accuracy. It has been found that it fluctuates slightly, but the value $1\cdot94$ is very close to the actual figures and will be used for future computations. This means that in a minute the heat of the sun falling at right angles to a surface one square centimetre in area would raise 1 gm. of water through $1\cdot94$°C., or $1\cdot94$ gm. through 1° C. The surface is assumed to be at the *mean* distance of the earth from the sun, 93,005,000 miles.

So far we have dealt with experimental evidence, but now it will be necessary to introduce a certain amount of theory. There is a law known as Stefan's Law which says that the sum total of radiation for a perfect radiator is proportional to the fourth power of the absolute temperature. By introducing certain constants known as Kurlbaum's constants, it has been found that a perfect radiator emits energy from each square centimetre of its surface at the rate of $76\cdot8 \times 10^{-12}\,T^4$ calories per minute, T denoting the absolute temperature. Hence this gives a measure of the sun's radiation if only we know the value of T.

Considering that the solar constant is $1\cdot94$ at the surface of the earth, can we find what it is at the surface of the sun ? This is a very simple problem because we know the relation between the radius of the sun and the distance of the earth from the sun. From the figures previously given the reader can work out this relation, and he will find that the distance of the earth from the sun is 215 times the sun's radius. Now, just as the volumes of spheres vary as the cubes of their diameters or radii, so their superficial areas vary as the *squares* of their radii. Imagine an enormous sphere with the centre of the sun as centre whose radius is a line drawn from the centre of the sun to the earth. This sphere would have an area 215^2 or 46,225 times the area of the surface of the sun, and if a small cone be drawn with its apex at the sun's centre, intersecting both the sun's surface and the surface of the sphere just mentioned, the area of the portion intersected at the distance of the earth is 46,225 times the area of the portion intersected at the surface of the sun. Hence, if we imagine that the former is 1 square centimetre in area, the area of the portion at the sun's surface is only 1/46,225 square centimetre. For this reason, $1\cdot94$ calories will represent the sun's output for each area of only 1/46,225 square centimetre, or each square centimetre will radiate 89,676 calories per minute. Assuming that the sun is a perfect radiator, we have the equation :

$$76\cdot8 \times 10^{-12}\,T^4 = 89{,}676, \text{ from which}$$
$$T^4 = 1168 \times 10^{12}.$$

Extracting the fourth root of the expression on the right of this equation, we find that T is 5845° K., or 5572° C., so this is the sun's surface temperature.

The assumption that the sun is a perfect radiator or that he radiates heat like a 'black body' is not quite valid, but is nearly so. A 'black body' is one that absorbs all radiation falling on it, infra-red, ultra-violet, X-rays, etc., neither reflecting nor transmitting any of this radiation. While no such bodies exist, many approximate to the ideal black body—including the sun. Stefan's Law applies to black body radiation only, and so the above result for the sun can be considered only approximately correct. Other methods have given results from about 5,800° C. to 5,927° C., and it is usual to assume a temperature of about 6,000° C. for the surface of the sun.

The Sun's Physical Appearance

Knowing that such a high temperature exists at the surface of the sun, we shall not be surprised at the appearance which he presents when examined with the aid of a small telescope. Readers may be warned at this point to exercise great care if they look at the sun through a telescope or even through binoculars. *Be sure to interpose a piece of smoked glass between the eyepiece of the telescope or whatever instrument is used, and your eye.** The object glass focuses the heat and light of the sun very close to the eye, and in some cases permanent injury has been done to the eye by the sun's heat when the precaution just mentioned had been neglected. The eyepieces of telescopes, but not of binoculars, are usually provided with one or more dark caps which can be screwed on to the eyepiece, and this acts like the smoked glass, but be sure that the cap is screwed on before you look at the sun through the telescope. Another way of observing the sun, without looking directly at his surface, is to hold a sheet of smooth white cardboard behind the eyepiece, and to rack the eyepiece out beyond its focal position. After a few trials of racking and holding the cardboard at a convenient distance, the sun's image will be seen sharply focused on the cardboard. Several observers can look on at the same time and see the sunspots very clearly, when they exist on the sun.

The visible surface of the sun is known as the *photosphere* (from the Greek *phos* light, meaning the light sphere), and is the region of the sunspots and faculæ about which something will now be said.

Sunspots and Faculæ

It is not always necessary to use a telescope to see the sunspots, because they are sometimes large enough to be seen with the naked eye (using smoked glass). There is a great diversity in the sizes of sunspots, some being only a few hundred miles in diameter and many probably less (but these cannot be seen even with the telescope), and others as much as 50,000 miles in diameter, or about six times the diameter of the earth. They look dark, but this is only by contrast with the brighter photosphere,

*Ordinary glass which has been smoked is not very satisfactory as the soot is liable to rub off. It is better to use coloured glass specially designed for the eyepieces of telescopes.

and they are by no means either dark or cold, when compared with terrestrial standards. The central part of a sunspot, known as the *umbra*, is darker than the lighter border, known as the *penumbra*. Sunspots are of no particular shape, though many of the more stable spots are circular, but they exhibit different shapes and also change their forms rapidly, suggesting that there must be terrific 'storms' on the sun's surface. Observations of these spots since 1610 have been investigated, and it has been shown that they run in cycles, the average interval between successive maxima being 11·2 years, but extreme values of 7·3 and 17·1 years have occurred. They rise from minimum spottedness more quickly than they decline, the periods on the average being 4½ and 6½ years. The last maximum took place about July of 1938. There are various theories about the causes of these changes in the frequency of sunspots, but there is still a considerable amount of doubt as to the real cause.

Sunspots have provided the astronomer with a very convenient method of measuring the rates of rotations of the sun in various parts, and have shown that the sun does not rotate like a solid body with the same angular velocity everywhere. It is true that spots have a motion of their own, independent of the sun's rotation, but it is very small— about 1 per cent of the motion due to rotation. It has been found that in the neighbourhood of the sun's equator the time of his rotation is just under 25 days, and in polar regions it is about 34 days. Spots cannot be used for finding the period of rotation in high latitudes because they seldom occur more than 30° from the equator, but in this latter case the spectroscope supplies the necessary information. The fact that the surface of the sun rotates with various velocities according to the latitude suggests that we are dealing with a gaseous body.

Large sunspots are associated with a number of terrestrial phenomena, such as magnetic storms, displays of the aurora, and even a slight increase in rainfall. Electrons are ejected with a high speed from the sun— so high that they reach the earth in less than two days—and the upper atmosphere is made luminous when they encounter it, the result being the Aurora Borealis in our hemisphere, or the Aurora Australis in the southern hemisphere. The effect of these electrons on the telegraphic system, on wireless sets, etc., is well known, and need not cause any surprise. It would be surprising if negative charges of electricity in our atmosphere were not attended by such disturbances. Perhaps it is not so obvious why an increased rainfall should follow sunspot activity, but from what we have said in the first chapter about the Wilson cloud chamber and the condensation of moisture on gaseous ions, we should expect that there would be an increased number of such in the atmosphere, due to the showers of electrons, and that they would form the nuclei for the condensation of moisture, resulting in increased rainfall. In this connection some mention should be made of the work of A. E. Douglass on the trunks of old trees, especially the sequoia. We should expect an increased growth during a moist period, and the work of Douglass shows that the 11-year sunspot cycle has actually manifested itself in an increase in the growth of trees, shown by the rings on their trunks. Here we have one of many instances of the wonderful correlation of results by men of science who are working in different spheres, and later on we shall read about other cases.

Near the sun's rim, or, as astronomers call it, the limb, large

irregular bright patches are usually visible in the telescope, and the name *faculæ* (from the Latin *faculæ*, little torches) is given to these patches. They are more easily seen near the limb because the background there is less bright than on other parts of the sun. They are above the photosphere and their temperature is from 100° C. to 200° C. higher than that of the photosphere. They are probably some form of clouds suspended in the solar atmosphere.

Above the photosphere lies the *reversing layer*, rightly so called, because it absorbs light from the photosphere underneath, and so forms the dark lines in the solar spectrum. Its thickness is from 100 to 200 miles, and its average temperature is a little lower than that of the photosphere.

The *chromosphere* (from the Greek *chroma*, colour), outside the reversing layer, is so named because of its scarlet colour which shows so distinctly during a total eclipse. It is composed chiefly of hydrogen and helium and also calcium, and it contains atoms that have lost an electron and so have become ionized (see Chapter I). It is several thousand miles thick and the *prominences* which arise from it sometimes attain heights of hundreds of thousands of miles. At ordinary times the prominences can be seen with a special apparatus which was used independently by Lockyer and Janssen in 1866, but during a total eclipse they are visible to the naked eye. They assume very varied forms, such as clouds, feathers or fountains, and some of them have an extraordinary resemblance to the giant reptiles of the Jurassic period. They are sometimes maintained for a time or they may change very rapidly. These great tongues of flame, consisting of incandescent gases, extend a long distance, probably some thousands of miles, into the chromosphere to which they are joined by columns of gas. The dimensions of a typical prominence are approximately as follows : length 125,000 miles, height 30,000 miles, thickness 6,000 miles. Within recent years they have been filmed by a special method, and when shown on the screen they present a wonderful and awe-inspiring sight.

The *corona* (from the Latin *corona*, a crown) is the outer envelope of the sun and can be seen best during the period of a total solar eclipse. In recent times it has been possible to see and photograph the corona in daylight with a special apparatus removed to the top of a mountain, where the lowest and most turbid layers of the atmosphere can be avoided. At the time of a total eclipse, when it is visible to the naked eye, it is a beautiful sight, looking like a pearly halo and emitting about half as much light as is emitted by the full moon. Several theories on the cause, of the corona have been elaborated, but there is no space to deal with these, and in any case, it must be admitted that its constitution and shape are problems still awaiting solution.

It is often thought that the study of the solar features is a matter for the professional astronomer with his powerful telescope, but amateur astronomers do very valuable work in this branch. Amongst the latter who specialize on solar work reference may be made to Mr. F. J. Sellers, Director of the Solar Section and a former President of the British Astronomical Association, Mr. A. M. Newbegin and Dr. M. A. Ellison. Papers on their work on sunspots, prominences, and other solar phenomena appear from time to time in the *Journal of the British Astronomical Association* and *Monthly Notices of the Royal Astronomical Society*, and are recognized as contributions of high scientific value.

C

How the Sun's Heat is Maintained

We are now in a position, after this brief survey of the sun's surface, to inquire how the heat of the sun is maintained without any intermission and practically at the same rate for hundreds of millions of years. If we ask what it is that burns in the sun we shall find that the question does not admit of an easy answer. It has been estimated that if the sun were composed of coal and had been lighted during the time of the first Pharaohs of Egypt, it would be nothing but a burnt-out ash by now. It must be remembered that when we speak of an object burning we think of it uniting with oxygen, but no such action takes place on the sun, and indeed the temperature is too high for such chemical action to occur. Complex compounds are broken up into elementary substances at a temperature of 6,000° C., and ordinary combustion is impossible in such circumstances. We shall examine some hypotheses which were advanced to explain how the sun developed and maintained his heat.

The Contraction Theory

About a century ago Helmholtz, a German physicist, explained the sun's output of heat by assuming that our luminary was once an enormous sphere of cool gas, which, however, under its own gravitation, started to contract. As a result of this contraction the gas in its interior underwent a rise in temperature, a simple illustration of which is found in the case of a bicycle or motor car pump. Everyone who has used such a pump is aware of the fact that the air inside increases in temperature by compression. When a gas is heated it tends to expand, and hence there would come a time when the contraction of the great gaseous sphere would be arrested by the increasing pressure of the heated gas in the interior. This would be a temporary cessation of contraction because the outer layers of the sun would radiate its energy, in the form of heat and light, into space, cooling would ensue, and a further contraction would occur, the process being repeated from time to time. It will be obvious that chemical action is entirely eliminated by this theory, the heat and light being due to gravitational energy which was released in the process of contraction.

A simple illustration of this principle is found in the case of falling bodies. When a body falls to the ground, thus approaching the centre of gravity of the earth, it does work, the amount of work being measured by the mass of the body multiplied by the distance through which it falls. On the other hand, if we want to raise a body from the surface of he earth, that is, to increase its distance from the earth's centre of gravity, we must use a certain amount of energy or spend work in doing so.

There was no fundamental error in Helmholtz's theory, and indeed such a process as he postulated probably occurs with many stars. The error lies in the fact that the method which he assumed to be responsible for supplying the heat of the sun would not suffice for the long period for which we know that our sun has existed. In fact, the theory would limit the life of the sun to a little over 20 million years. It was shown that the present output of solar energy would demand that his radius must decrease each year by three parts in a million, and such a change would not be noticeable over the period of human history, but, when we

deal with the geological time-scale, extending over a thousand million years, such a contraction would be too rapid. Incidentally, the geologist could not accept the contraction theory as an explanation of the heat of the sun, because the evidence of the rocks showed conclusively that the earth was many times older than the relatively short period of 20 million years, and also that the earliest forms of life were much more than twenty times this number of years in existence.

Meteors

There is another theory to explain the heat of the sun—the theory that his surface is being continuously bombarded by meteoric matter. We have all seen meteors—commonly known as 'shooting stars'—which are minute specks, often as small as grains of sand, that strike the upper regions of the atmosphere with velocities varying from 10 to 45 miles a second. It may seem remarkable that anyone could suggest the possibility of such bodies or even larger ones being responsible for the heat of the sun, but the theory is not so far-fetched as it appears at first. Before examining this theory it will be necessary to digress to show the relation between heat and mechanical energy. When this is understood it will be easier to follow the arguments relating to the effect of meteoric matter striking the sun.

Energy and Heat

Some of us have tried the experiment of rubbing a brass button or other metal on a piece of wood and then applying the metal to the back of the hand. We have discovered that a considerable temperature is produced in this way, and all that has happened is that mechanical energy has appeared in the form of heat. It may be inferred from this that heat is a form of energy and careful experiments have been conducted to determine the relation between the expenditure of a certain amount of energy and the amount of heat produced. As the metric system is used by physicists, and is much more convenient for computational purposes than the English system, which is still in use amongst engineers, we shall follow the usual practice and give the results in the metric system, known as the c.g.s. system, *i.e.*, the centimetre-gramme-second.

The unit of work is known as the *erg* and is the work done when a force of one dyne (1/980 gm.) moves its point of application over a distance of one centimetre in the direction of the force. Expressed in another way we can say that an erg is the work done when a mass equal to the weight of $1/g$ gm. is lifted against gravitation through 1 cm. The value of g, the acceleration of a falling body, is about 980 cm. (32 feet) per second per second, that is, a falling body increases its velocity by about 980 cm. per second each second of its fall. Although the value of g varies a little in different parts of the earth, it will be seen from the last definition of an erg that its value remains the same whatever the place on the surface of the earth may be, because, though the weight of one gramme varies, so does the value of gravitation against which the dyne moves. The name *absolute unit* of work has been assigned to the erg.

It has been found from a number of experiments that the expenditure of $4 \cdot 186 \times 10^7$ ergs is equivalent to one calorie, or in other words, if

4·186 × 10^7 ergs are converted into heat, the amount of heat would be sufficient to raise one gramme of water through one degree Centigrade, or, more correctly, to raise the gramme of water from 14·5° C. to 15·5° C. (see p. 29 for the definition of a calorie). As an illustration of this, suppose we could fire a bullet from a rifle and that the bullet had the energy 4·186 × 10^7 ergs ; if it were brought to rest by a target *and all the heat developed were concentrated in the bullet* from which it could be transferred into a gramme of water, the temperature of the water would rise one degree Centigrade. In the English system, 1,496 foot-pounds of work, expended in the production of heat, would develop a quantity of heat sufficient to raise one pound of water through one degree Centigrade. (A foot-pound is the work done in raising a weight of one pound through a foot.)

The energy of a moving body is measured by the product of half its mass and the square of its velocity. Thus, if a body weighing 10 gm. is moving with a velocity of 2,000 cm. per sec., the energy possessed by the moving body is $\frac{1}{2}$ × 10 × 2,000^2 = 2 × 10^7 ergs.

Heat Generated by Meteoric Impact

Let us consider the case of a meteor weighing 1 gm. and moving with a velocity of 68 × 10^5 cm. per sec., which is a little over 40 miles a second. The energy of this meteor is 231 × 10^{11} ergs. Now consider the energy of a body weighing 100 lbs. and moving with a velocity of 1,000 feet per second. On first appearance it seems that this body should have considerably more energy than the small body weighing 1 gm., which is about the forty five-thousandth part of 100 lbs. The fact is, however, that the energy of each body is practically the same, that of the heavier body being a little less than the energy of 1 gm. This is due to the fact that the energy of motion increases as the *square* of the velocity, so that bodies with high velocities, though not very massive, may possess enormous amounts of energy.

Now let us apply this reasoning to the sun. We know that bodies attracted by the sun from great distances will strike his surface with a velocity of 392 miles a second, or nearly 631 × 10^5 cm. per sec. Hence each gramme would deliver to the sun 2 × 10^{15} ergs on impact, and we shall inquire whether sufficient meteoric matter can strike the sun's surface to account for the output of heat which it emits.

The diameter of the sun is 864,000 miles, or 139 × 10^9 cms, and as the area of a sphere is πd^2, π being 3·14159 and d the diameter, the area of the sun's surface is 607 × 10^{20} square cm. It has been shown that each square centimetre radiates 89,676 calories each minute, so that the total radiation per minute from the sun's surface is 544 × 10^{25} calories. We have seen that the expenditure of 4·186 × 10^7 ergs is equivalent to one calorie, and hence in each minute the sun radiates away (544 × 10^{25}) × (4·186 × 10^7) = 228 × 10^{33} ergs. As each gramme of meteoric matter would be responsible for 2 × 10^{15} ergs on colliding with the sun, it would be necessary for (228 × 10^{33})/(2 × 10^{15}) = 114 × 10^{18} gm. of meteoric matter to strike the surface of the sun each minute, which is the same as 6 × 10^{25} gm. a year. Now the mass of the sun at present is 2 × 10^{33} gm., and hence in a little over 30 million years the sun would double his mass if his heat were supplied by meteoric matter ! It is

sufficient to produce these quantitative results to show the absurdity of such a theory. (It has been assumed that the sun's surface gravity would remain the same—an assumption which is not correct—but the figures are sufficiently accurate for our purpose.)

Energy Supplied by Nuclear Disintegration

The old riddle concerning the sources of the solar radiation is no longer a riddle since the discovery of the enormous amount of energy which is liberated in nuclear disintegration. If the ordinary radio-active elements, uranium, thorium, etc., were in sufficient abundance in the sun there would be no difficulty in explaining his output of heat, but it is certain that there is not enough of these to account for an energy of 228×10^{33} ergs per minute. There is no necessity to depend on these radio-active elements for an explanation, because the transformation of the ordinary more stable elements is sufficient for the purpose. Although such transformations in the laboratory are on an almost microscopic scale, the conditions in the interior of the sun, which has a temperature of about 20,000,000°C. near his centre, are just those which produce nuclear transformations on an enormous scale, thus providing all the energy that is required for the sun's output, and incidentally sufficient to continue providing it for many thousands of millions of years.

It is well known that the molecules of a gas are in a continuous state of motion, jostling one another continuously, and that their rate of motion increases with increasing temperature. This explains the increase of pressure of a gas confined in a certain volume when the temperature rises. It is not difficult to imagine that the very high temperature in the interior of the sun produces such agitation that not only is matter broken up into molecules and atoms, but even the electrons will be stripped off the atoms, leaving the bare nuclei. The process does not end with the bare nuclei because further impacts on them will lead to more far-reaching results, and transformations with the liberation of enormous stores of energy will ensue. Before discussing this in detail, a few words will be said about a chemical term which is employed in explaining the nuclear reactions.

There are several chemical actions which are able to proceed only in the presence of small quantities (and sometimes minute quantities) of a third substance which itself remains unchanged at the conclusion of the action. These cases are included under the name of *catalytic* actions, and the third substance is known as the *catalyst* or *catalytic agent*. A well-known instance is the action of manganese dioxide mixed with potassium chlorate. On heating the mixture, oxygen is evolved at a much lower temperature than occurs when no manganese dioxide is used. The manganese dioxide is the catalytic agent in this case, and there are many other similar cases where the catalytic agent plays a prominent part in chemical reactions.

The sequence of nuclear transformations which are supposed to take place in the sun are shown in the following table. The symbols C^{12}, N^{15}, etc., are used to denote the atomic weights of the elements, and it should be noticed that these do not always correspond to the atomic weights which are found in works on chemistry. The reason is because

we are often dealing with isotopes, of which a brief explanation was given on p. 18, and hence the atomic weights may differ from those given for the ordinary state of the element. An explanation of the table follows, and it will be seen that the nuclear transformation process works in a cycle which is repeated indefinitely.

Nuclear Reactions which Generate Energy in the Sun.

$C^{12} + H^1 \longrightarrow N^{13} + \gamma\text{-ray.}$ $N^{13} \longrightarrow C^{13} + e^+.$ $C^{13} + H^1 \longrightarrow N^{14} + \gamma\text{-ray.}$
$N^{14} + H^1 \longrightarrow O^{15} + \gamma\text{-ray.}$ $O^{15} \longrightarrow N^{15} + e^+.$ $N^{15} + H^1 \longrightarrow C^{12} + He^4.$
$C^{12} + H^1 \longrightarrow N^{13} + \gamma\text{-ray,}$ and so on.

The following is an explanation of the above table :

Starting the series with ordinary carbon C^{12}, a collision with a proton, denoted by H^1, takes place. The orbital electrons have been removed in the conditions of very high temperature and only nuclei are left, but as these contain practically all the mass of an atom, no appreciable difference in the atomic weight occurs. The result of the collision is the formation of the lighter isotope of nitrogen, N^{13}, and the liberation of energy in the form of a γ-ray. This is not mere theory because such a reaction has been obtained in the laboratory. The nucleus of N^{13} emits a positron, marked e^+, and becomes the nucleus of the heavier carbon isotope, C^{13}. This carbon atom is then struck by a proton, H^1, and becomes ordinary nitrogen, N^{14} with a γ-ray radiation. The nucleus of N^{14} collides with another proton, and as a result there is produced the oxygen isotope, O^{15} and a γ-ray radiation also occurs. This oxygen atom then emits a positron and becomes N^{15} which is struck by a proton and is transformed into C^{12} and the helium nucleus. The atom C^{12} is then struck by a proton and the cycle recommences to be repeated. As will be seen, the process consists in a transformation of elements.

On examining the table it is seen that a nucleus of either carbon or nitrogen, in the form of different isotopes, occurs in every reaction, and that they act like the catalysts of the chemist, though the similarity should not be pressed too far, but it can be regarded as a useful analogy. The real result of the six reactions is that collisions with four protons have ended by producing a helium nucleus, so that the whole process can be summed up by saying that hydrogen has been transformed into helium by the high temperature, aided by the catalytic action of carbon and nitrogen.

Past and Future of the Sun

Even if the sun contains large quantities of hydrogen, it would be impossible for the reactions to occur without the presence of carbon or nitrogen and, of course, of the high temperature. There is sufficient hydrogen in the sun—probably about 35 per cent of the sun's mass consists of hydrogen—to enable the reactions to go on for many thousand of millions of years, and there is also a sufficient amount of carbon and nitrogen to ensure the catalytic action for an enormous period. Will the high temperature continue or will the sun's temperature gradually decrease until a time comes when the nuclear processes are no longer possible ? With the present interior temperature of the sun it has been estimated that five million years are required for the complete cycle just referred to, but of course countless cycles are commencing every moment and count-

less others ending every moment, so that there is no interruption in the output of energy. If, however, the temperature of the sun's interior decreased, there would be a diminution of the rate of reaction, the cycle requiring more than five million years, and the net effect would, apparently, be cumulative, the temperature falling continually and finally very rapidly. The problem is not quite so simple as it seems, however, as the following considerations will show.

Under the conditions of high temperature and high density prevailing in the interior of the sun, radiation is absorbed by the layers of hydrogen and helium, but helium absorbs the radiation much more effectively than hydrogen. For this reason the more rapidly helium is formed, the more energy liberated in the reactions is trapped, or the more difficult it is for the energy to find its way through the opaque helium layers to the surface of the sun and from thence out into the depths of space. The result is that the temperature *increases* and this increased temperature is responsible for additional nuclear reactions so that the temperature of the sun goes on increasing with time. While this increase in temperature is going on, the hydrogen content is decreasing, because, as the table shows, although hydrogen is transmuted into helium, the process is not reversible. It has been estimated that throughout the whole geological period, during which the sun lost about one per cent of its hydrogen, the increase in the sun's output of heat was sufficient to raise the earth's mean temperature by only a few degrees—an indication of the gradual process of rise in the sun's temperature.

Although the process is very slow, yet, looking into the future, we can see the temperature of the sun so high that the temperature on the earth might unfit it for life in the higher forms, and finally for life in any condition, animal or vegetable. The same thing would apply to the other planets in the course of myriads of geological ages, at least to those that are now cold. As we shall see later, the planet Mercury is in the stage where its temperature is much too high to support life such as we know on the earth, and perhaps this will be the ultimate fate of all the planets, if indeed any of them, outside the earth, have life on them at present. With increasing temperature of the sun there will also be an increase in his radius, so if there are any intelligent beings left on our earth after many thousands of millions of years, they will see the sun a little larger than we do to-day.

The story does not end with a sun increasing in size and also in temperature until it becomes a mere gas bubble. A limit is reached when all the hydrogen content has been used up or rather transmuted into helium, and hence no more fuel is available to supply the energy. Deprived of this source of energy, the sun will start to contract and in doing so will develop a certain amount of energy which will maintain some of its heat for a time, but such a method is very ephemeral on the cosmic time-scale. The doom of the sun is inevitable and it will shrink to smaller and smaller dimensions, gradually approaching its death and emitting a mere fraction of the light and heat which it was once capable of doing. The end comes when it collapses into a white dwarf—of which there are a number now known in the universe—an extremely small star with an enormous density, owing to the fragments of atoms being jammed together in a condition of high concentration. We shall refer to this type of star later in this book when we come to deal with the stars in general.

Thus we can summarize the future history of our sun by saying that his temperature will increase until life on our planet will be exterminated —a view contrary to that usually held until recently, as it was believed that our sun was cooling. If we could imagine some being on the earth endowed with immortality he would see various forms of life slowly disappear until only the lowest micro-organisms survived. Even these in time would succumb when the oceans were turned into vapour and the earth was enveloped in a canopy of clouds. Then after an immense time he would see the enlarged sun gradually shrink and the earth would become cooler, life in very primitive forms appearing in the oceans, and higher forms developing and inhabiting both sea and land. Whether such life would follow the evolutionary course that it followed during the geological ages is impossible to say, but in any case its ultimate fate would be the same—extermination—not through heat but because of the intense cold which would freeze the oceans and convert the earth into a great mass of ice. This would be the final stage ; there would be no resuscitation of a moribund sun and hence no revival of life on a dead world which would still continue its revolutions round its primary and share its motion through the galaxy. To an inhabitant of some planet of a far-off star, if he had some super-optical equipment, the earth would present the appearance of an insignificant planet drifting ghostlike through space, a sphere of ice and snow, from which all life and activity had long since vanished, and to which such life and activity could never return.

CHAPTER III

THE EARTH

A Model of the Sun and Earth

THE EARTH IS A MUCH SMALLER BODY THAN THE SUN, AND A USEFUL model on a small scale which will enable us to visualize the relation between them is as follows :

Imagine that the earth is a billiard ball 2 inches in diameter. On the same scale the sun would be represented by a sphere just over 18 feet in diameter at a distance of 650 yards. Pluto, the outermost planet of the solar system, which was discovered in 1930, would be more than 14 miles away from the large sphere, on the same scale. This model gives us some conception of the immensity of the planetary distances from the sun, but rather a poor conception of the distances of the stars. On the same scale the nearest star would be about 100,000 miles distant.

Dimensions of the Earth and its Distance from the Sun

The earth's distance from the sun is not always the same, varying slightly owing to the elliptical orbit that it describes in its annual journey round the sun. Its greatest distance, which it attains about July 4 each year, is 94,561,000 miles, and its least distance, which it reaches about January 4, is 91,449,000 miles. These two positions are known as aphelion and perihelion, respectively, from the Greek *apo* away from, and *helios* the sun, and also *peri*, round, about, with the same Greek noun. The mean distance of the earth from the sun is 93,005,000 miles.

The diameter of the earth is not the same everywhere because, owing to the rotation of the earth on its axis, there is a slight bulge in equatorial regions. This bulge is due to centrifugal force, that is, the force which urges anything on a rotating body to fly off from the centre. We see an illustration of centrifugal force in a rotating wheel, say, of a car, which throws off the mud from the tyres, and the greater the speed of the wheel, the greater is the velocity with which the mud is ejected. If the earth rotated 17 times as fast as it does at present (i.e., over 17,000 m.p.h. or 25,900 feet per second at the equator) nothing in equatorial regions would remain on its surface, the centrifugal force just balancing the gravitational pull of the earth on bodies which lay at the equator. (See Appendix II.) The centrifugal force increases from the poles, where it is zero, to the equator, where it is a maximum. Although unable to eject anything from the earth with its present speed of rotation, it is nevertheless responsible for producing a difference in the weight of a body, as measured at the equator and in latitudes further north or south. It would be necessary to measure the weight in all cases by means of a spring balance, not with ordinary scales, because the weight on each scale pan would be equally affected by the centrifugal force in all places, and hence no difference in the gravitational pull of the earth for a mass could be detected.

The effect of the earth's rotation is to cause the equatorial diameter to be nearly 27 miles longer than its polar diameter. The figures for each, based on very accurate determinations, are :

Earth's equatorial diameter 7926·70 miles.
,, polar ,, 7900·02 ,,

Because of this polar compression and equatorial bulge the earth is not an exact sphere but is known as an *oblate spheroid.*

The daily rotation of the earth on its polar diameter is the cause of the phenomenon of day and night, the sun, moon and stars *appearing* to move in a direction opposite to that in which the earth rotates—in other words, while the earth rotates from west to east, the heavenly bodies all seem to move round the earth from east to west.

The orbital motion of the earth round the sun is the cause of the seasons. It is not generally realized that the rotation of the earth is also responsible, in a certain sense, for the seasons, as we shall now explain.

The Earth's Axis points nearly in a Constant Direction

Most readers are aware of the fact that if a body is rotating, some resistance is offered by the body to any change in the direction of its axis of rotation. For instance, if a bicycle is suspended by a rope attached to the crossbar, and the back wheel is rotated rapidly, when an attempt is made to turn the bicycle so that the axle of the wheel points in some other direction, there seems to be a force opposing the operator. If the wheel is not rotating, no such force is experienced, and the faster it rotates the greater the force is found to be. This principle is exemplified in many important problems in celestial mechanics, and is known as the *principle of the conservation of angular momentum.* The best way of illustrating it is by means of a gyroscope. It will be found that if the heavy wheel is not spinning there is no resistance offered to turning the axle of this wheel in any direction, but when it is spinning, or rotating, to use a more correct

term, a certain amount of resistance is experienced when the axle is
tilted so that its direction in space is altered.   On the other hand, the
gyroscope can be carried round a central point or moved about in various
ways *so long as the direction of the axle is not changed*, without any resistance
being experienced.

The same principle applies to a planet in rotation.   We can think of the
earth rotating on an imaginary axis running from pole to pole, and just

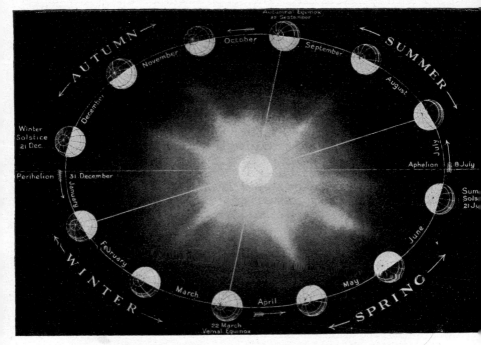

Fig. 10. Owing to the earth's axial spin the polar axis points in nearly the same
direction in space for a long time.   In the winter of the northern hemisphere
this hemisphere is tilted away from the sun and receives the solar rays
obliquely, but the southern hemisphere is exposed to more direct radiation
at the same time, and hence its summer corresponds with the winter of
the northern hemisphere.   At the vernal and autumnal equinoxes neither
hemisphere is tilted towards the sun more than the other, and at these
periods every place on the earth's surface has 12 hours day and 12 hours night.

like a bicycle wheel or a gyroscope, some force is required to alter the
direction of the axis.   For the present we shall assume that there is no
such force capable of changing the direction of the earth's polar diameter
and that it always points to the same place in space, or in other words,
that it always remains parallel to itself, while the earth revolves round
the sun in the course of a year.   It will be shown later that this assumption
is not strictly accurate.

The Seasons

Fig. 10 will explain the succession of the seasons, but a small model
made out of a sphere about a foot in diameter would give a much better

conception of the phenomenon than diagrams. The table on which the experiments are conducted can be regarded as the plane of the ecliptic, a light from an electric torch can be used to represent the sun, and the sphere, which represents the earth, can be carried round the light, so that its axis of rotation always points approximately in the same direction. This axis of rotation should not be perpendicular to the plane of the table but inclined to it at an angle of about 66½°. The actual value of this angle for illustrative purposes, however, need not be measured accurately, and can be taken at any convenient value, larger than 66½° if necessary.

The polar axis of the earth is inclined at an angle of about 66½° to the plane of the ecliptic and this angle remains practically the same over long periods of time. When the northern hemisphere is tilted away from the sun, as happens during its winter, the colder conditions are not due to the fact that this portion of the earth is at a slightly greater distance from the sun than the southern hemisphere, which is tilted towards the sun at the same time and enjoys summer conditions. The chief reason for the colder conditions is found in the *obliquity of the sun's rays when they fall on the northern hemisphere.* This may not seem very obvious at first, but a good illustration, which will make it clearer than a prolonged explanation, is easily obtained by casting the light from a torch on a piece of cardboard a few feet away from the torch. Hold the cardboard first of all so that the rays of light fall perpendicular to the plane of the cardboard and notice the size of the illuminated portion. Now tilt the cardboard so that the rays fall on it obliquely. It will be seen that a larger patch of the cardboard is illuminated in the latter case than in the former, though the amount of light (and heat also, if we include the heat from the torch) emanating from the torch is the same in each case. When the rays of light fall obliquely the same quantity is distributed over a larger area, and hence

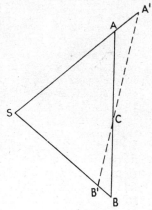

Fig. 11. Rays of light from a source S fall on a line AB the centre of which is C. In the first case let SC be perpendicular to AB—a representation of the light and heat from the sun falling on equatorial regions at the spring or autumn equinox. Now rotate the line round its centre into the position A'B'. The radiation which previously fell on CB now falls on CB' which is less than CB, and hence the same amount of heat falls on a smaller length, so that the quantity received per unit area is greater in the latter case. The amount received per unit area on CA' is obviously less than on CA. The same argument applies if we consider a cone of radiation instead of a triangle.

any definite area, say a square inch, will receive less light than it will when the rays fall perpendicular to the cardboard.

While this experiment appears to show very simply why the succession of summer and winter occurs, readers may enquire whether the portion of the cardboard tilted *towards* the torch also receives less radiation for any given area than it does in the case of the direct impact of the rays. It almost seems that the experiment proves too much, but a glance at Fig. 11 will show why the southern hemisphere, which we shall suppose

to be tilted towards the sun, receives more light and heat. To simplify the problem it will be sufficient to consider the radiation falling on a line, the middle point of which, C, represents the equator. Instead of giving a geometrical proof, the diagram is drawn to scale and the explanation underneath shows that the principle of the model just described is perfectly sound.

Another factor contributing to the phenomenon of summer and winter is the atmospheric absorption of the sun's radiation. The density of the atmosphere decreases as we ascend from the surface of the earth, and this decrease is rapid. A good rule to remember is that if we ascend in distances which increase in arithmetical progression, the density of the atmosphere decreases in geometrical progression. It has been found that the density at a height of $3\frac{1}{2}$ miles (18,480 feet) is 0·5 that at sea level. Ascend another $3\frac{1}{2}$ miles and the density decreases to $(0·5)^2$ or to 0·25 that at sea level, and so on. For this reason if the sun's rays reach the surface of the earth when the sun is nearly overhead, or in the zenith, as this position is described, there will be much less atmospheric absorption of his radiation than when he is near the horizon, because in the latter case the rays are passing through strata of the atmosphere which, taken on the whole, are more dense than when the sun is in the zenith. It is only necessary to notice the rise of temperature during the day to obtain confirmation of this principle. Although this absorption is a factor in the phenomenon of summer and winter, it is of much less importance than the obliquity of impact of the sun's radiation on the earth's surface.

It has been assumed that the polar axis of the earth points in a constant direction, and for many practical purposes this may be assumed, for example, in explaining the seasons. If we are dealing with long periods it is by no means correct to say that the polar axis points towards the same place in the heavens, and we shall proceed to explain why it changes its position.

Precession of the Equinoxes

Terrestrial objects, often toys, are very useful for explaining some abstruse problems in celestial mechanics, and we shall utilize the ordinary spinning top to describe a phenomenon named *the precession of the equinoxes*, which was known to the ancient astronomers, though the cause of it was not known to them.

When a top is spinning it frequently slopes from the upright position and spins while its head moves round in a circle of its own, irrespective of the circle described by its rotation. In fact, we can describe the top as tracing out a cone in space, the bottom point of the top being the apex of the cone. This is a well-known phenomenon but the explanation of it involves rather difficult mathematics and it is not proposed to deal with this. It will suffice to accept the motion of the top as an established fact, and also to accept the gravitational attraction of the earth on the top as a contributory factor in the phenomenon to which the name *precession* is given. When the spinning ceases the top falls. It may also be noticed that when the top is nearing the end of its spin it 'nods' or wobbles, and this is also due to the same causes.

We have seen that the earth's polar axis is inclined to the ecliptic at an angle of about $66\frac{1}{2}°$, and as the polar axis is perpendicular to the plane

of the equator, the equator is inclined at an angle of $23\frac{1}{2}°$ to the ecliptic. If we could imagine that the earth had no rotation, the pull of the sun and moon on its equatorial bulge would tend to make the equator and ecliptic coincide. The reason is that the attractions on this bulge (which is very slightly nearer the sun and moon than the other portions of the earth) being a little greater on the average than on other parts of the earth, tend to pull it in such a way that it approaches the ecliptic. The moon does not move quite in the ecliptic, her orbit being tilted to it at an angle of more than 5°, but her attraction co-operates with that of the sun in the effect just described. If a stout piece of cardboard is attached to a sphere, so that the cardboard, slipping over the surface of the sphere, forms a plane like the plane of the equator, it will illustrate the principle. Imagine the sphere pivoted at its centre and someone pulling with a piece of string on the edge of the cardboard. It is obvious that he could easily tilt the whole apparatus into any position and make the plane of the cardboard coincide with any plane that he wanted. From what has been previously said about rotating bodies, it may be inferred that the sphere would not be easily tilted from one position to another if it were spinning rapidly on an axis at right angles to the plane of the cardboard.

Owing to the earth's rotation the attraction of the sun and moon on the equatorial bulge cannot easily tilt the equator to make it coincide with the ecliptic. The effect, however, is very similar to that of the pull of the earth on the spinning top ; while it tends to tilt the top so that its axis (an imaginary line from the point through its centre of gravity) approaches a horizontal position, the spin of the top prevents this and precession takes place. Instead of the earth's equator being pulled into the ecliptic, the axis performs a slow conical motion around a line joining the poles of the ecliptic, a complete precessional motion taking place in about 26,000 years.

Nutation

The moon, although very much less massive than the sun, is so close to the earth that her effect in producing precession is greater than that of the sun, and she is responsible for another small effect which will be briefly described.

The moon's orbit, inclined at more than 5° to the ecliptic, has two points of intersection with the ecliptic, known as the nodes. These nodes have a motion of their own round the ecliptic which they complete in a little less than 19 years, and during this time the inclination of the moon's orbit to the *equator* varies from about $18\frac{1}{2}°$ to $28\frac{1}{2}°$. Obviously, her effect on the equatorial regions of the earth will also vary a little with different inclinations, and hence a variation in the precession occurs. The result of this is that the curve described by the earth's axis is not a perfect circle but fluctuates a little, the pole 'nodding' slightly. The term *nutation* (from the Latin *nutare*, to nod) is applied to this phenomenon.

The effect of precession is that the celestial equator, or the plane in which the terrestrial equatorial plane intersects the heavens, swings slowly westward, maintaining nearly the same inclination to the ecliptic. As a result the points of intersection of equator and ecliptic move westward along the ecliptic at the rate of 50·26 seconds of arc each year. One of these points of intersection, the vernal equinox (the other is known as the autumnal equinox), is a fundamental point of reference for the

heavenly bodies, and this motion produces a number of complications in describing the positions of the stars from year to year. One important effect may be noticed. At present the earth's axis points nearly to the pole star, being only 1° from it, and, owing to precession, it will continue to approach it until A.D. 2,100 when it will be only 28′ from it. After

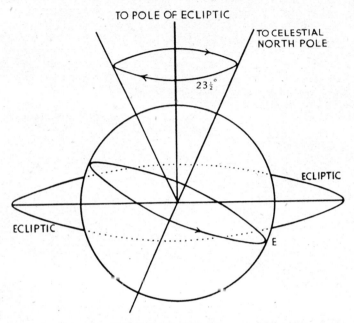

FIG. 12. THE EARTH'S PRECESSIONAL MOTION

The attraction of the sun and moon, the moon especially, on the protuberant portions of the earth in its equatorial regions, tends to bring the earth's equator E nearer to the plane of the ecliptic. Owing to the earth's rotation an effect similar to that which is seen in a gyroscope takes place. The axis of the earth has a slow conical motion around the line joining the poles of the ecliptic.

that it will recede from the pole star. About 3,000 B.C. α Draconis was the pole star and in A.D. 14,000 Vega will hold this honour. (See Fig. 12.)

How the Earth's Size is Measured

Before finding the distances, dimensions and masses of other heavenly bodies, it is necessary to make accurate calculations about the size and mass of the earth. To do so we must utilize the observations of the stars, so it is true to say that mutual assistance is essential in the realm of astronomy, the stars helping us to measure the earth's dimensions, and the earth providing the basis for finding the distances of the stars. A short explanation of the method for determining the earth's circumference and from this its diameter follows.

The zenith distance of a body at any place on the earth's surface is important and should be understood before proceeding. The diagram,

Fig. 13, shows two observers O and O′ looking at a star S which may be taken to be at an infinite distance in comparison with the small diameter of the earth. For this reason, if two observers could look at a star (not a comparatively close planet) from two places at the antipodes, the lines drawn from each one to the star would be parallel, or so nearly so that no instrument, however delicate, could possibly detect the smallest deviation from parallelism. The angle between the lines drawn from the observer to the centre of the earth, produced upwards, and to the star, is known as the star's zenith distance, and the complement of the zenith distance, that is,

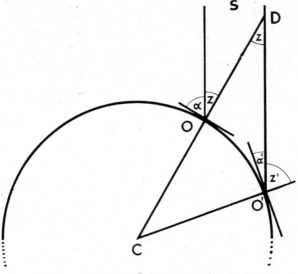

FIG. 13. FINDING THE SIZE OF THE EARTH

If two observers on the same meridian observe a star when it is crossing the meridian, the difference in the altitude of the star at each place of observation is the same as the angle C at the earth's centre subtended by the arc OO′ which connects the two observers. Knowing the value of the angle C, and also the length of the arc OO′, the length of an arc of one degree on the earth's surface can be ascertained. Multiplying this by 360 gives the earth's circumference.

$90°$ – zenith distance, is known as the star's altitude. Zenith distance and altitude are marked z and α in the diagram. To make the problem as simple as possible it will be assumed for the present that the earth is a sphere, not an oblate spheroid.

Imagine that an arc of a circle joins the two observers O and O′ and that the plane of this circle passes through the centre C of the earth. Produce CO to meet the line drawn from O′ to the star at D. Because OS and O′S are parallel, the angle at D is obviously z. In the triangle CDO′ the external angle $z′$ is equal to the sum of the angles C and z, or $z′-z=C$. Hence the angle subtended at the centre of the earth by the arc OO′ is simply the difference between the zenith distances of the star at O and O′, or, since $\alpha = 90° - z$, and $\alpha′ = 90° - z′$, the difference of the altitudes can be used.

By taking the differences of the altitudes or zenith distances of a star

as seen by each observer, the angle C at the centre of the earth is known, and it is then only necessary to measure the length of the arc OO' to find how many miles or kilometres correspond to a certain angle at the earth's centre. As a circle subtends 360° at its centre, a simple calculation gives the length of the circumference of the circle, which is practically the same, in the case under consideration, as the length of the earth's circumference. It has been found that the length of the arc subtending 1° at the centre that the earth is not the same everywhere, as we might expect from the fact that the earth is not a perfect sphere. In polar regions a degree of latitude is 69·41 English miles ; in the latitude of London it is 69·13 and in equatorial regions it is 68·70. If we take 69 miles as an average and multiply this by 360 we find 24,800 miles for the circumference of the earth. Dividing this by π, or 3·14159, the diameter is found to be 7,907 miles, which is not far from the mean of the polar and equatorial diameters.

Eratosthenes was the first to measure the circumference of the earth with any pretence to accuracy. About 250 B.C., he used the sun for this purpose, not a star, but the principle is precisely the same. He knew that at the summer solstice the sun at noon threw no shadow at Syene (the modern Assuan), while at Alexandria the shadow on a sundial at the same time indicated that the sun was 7·2° from the zenith. Measuring the distance between Syene and Alexandria and multiplying this distance by 50, because 7·2° is 1/50th of the angle subtended at the centre of a circle by the circumference, he found that the circumference of the earth was 250,000 stadia. There is some doubt about the length of the stadium. If Eratosthenes used the Greek stadium, which was 606·75 feet, the circumference was over 28,000 miles, but if he used another stadium, 40 of which were equal to the Egyptian *schoinus,* the length of the circumference would be 24,662 miles. If the latter stadium were used it shows a wonderful triumph of scientific calculation for the time in which Eratosthenes lived. In connection with this computation the following points should be noticed. The position of ancient Alexandria was, 31° 11′ N. lat., and 29° 52′ E. long., while that of Assuan was 24° 20′ N. lat., and 32° 35′ E. long., so that the two places were not on the same meridian. This fact would vitiate the results to a small extent.

How the Earth is Weighed

Different methods have been used to find the mass of the earth. The first method, which was used by Bouger in Peru in 1735 and later by Maskelyne, consisted in finding the deflections of a plumb line by a mountain, thus affording a comparison between the attractions of the earth and mountain. Knowing the nature of the minerals in the mountain and also its volume, its mass could be estimated, and hence the mass of the earth. In theory the method is simple, but in practice the experiment is rather difficult to carry out accurately, and better methods have been adopted which depend on the force of attraction between two known masses.

Attraction of Masses Measured by the Torsion Balance

The torsion balance is used to find the value of a very small force, and consists of a light horizontal bar suspended by a quartz fibre. The force required to displace the bar through any angle is first found when two

small balls are fixed one on each end of the rod. This is done with great accuracy, and then the small balls, attached to each end of the bar, are attracted by two large balls placed near them. The apparatus is placed in an air-tight vessel from which the air is then exhausted, and precautions are taken to ensure a constant temperature in the vessel. The two heavier balls, which are generally lead (the small balls on the bar were first of all made of lead and later of gold) are brought near the small balls, but are outside the vessel, attracting them through the glass. The displacement is so small that very refined methods for measuring it must be used, and it is at this stage that errors are liable to occur. Knowing the displacement it is easy to find the force of attraction between the two large and two small balls. The theory of the problem is simple and depends on the law of gravitation : "Every particle of matter in the universe attracts every other particle with a force which is proportional to the product of their masses, and which varies inversely as the square of the distance between their centres." We have already seen the application of this law in the Introduction.

The two balls are used to balance the light rod, and it will be sufficient to consider the attraction of one ball on another. Let m be the mass of the heavy ball and m' that of the light ball, and let r be the distance between their centres, the units being in the c.g.s. (i.e., centimetre-gram-second) system. The attraction of the larger ball on the smaller one is proportional to mm'/r^2, and it must be noticed that this is not the actual force of attraction between the balls, but is *proportional* to the attractive force. If M is the mass of the earth and R its radius, its attraction for the smaller body, denoted by F, is proportional to Mm'/R^2. The ratio of f to F is

$$f/F = mm'/r^2 \div Mm'/R^2 = mR^2/Mr^2$$

Now F is simply the weight of the smaller ball, and as f has been found by the experiment, the ratio f/F is known. Since m, r and R are also known, M is determined from the above equation.

The most accurate determinations of the mass of the earth agree on the value $5 \cdot 98 \times 10^{27}$ grams. Knowing the radius of the earth and hence its volume, its density is found to be $5 \cdot 52$. (See Appendix III for a more detailed mathematical explanation.)

Variation in the Value of Gravity

On the surface of the earth the value of g (the usual abbreviation for the value of gravity) is about 981 cm./sec.^{2}, or $32 \cdot 2$ ft./sec.^{2}*, but it varies a little. One reason, as we have seen, is that in equatorial regions the centrifugal force is greater than at any other place on the earth, and this diminishes g. In addition, a body at the equator is at a greater distance from the centre of the earth than it is elsewhere on the earth's surface, and this also contributes to a diminution of g. A simple formula which is sufficiently accurate for all practical purposes, to find g at any latitude φ, is

$$g = 980 \cdot 621 - 2 \cdot 589 \cos 2\varphi$$

*The reader will sometimes meet with this form for expressing acceleration. Velocity is defined as the ratio of length to time, or l/t, and hence the dimensions of velocity are 1 in length and -1 in time. Acceleration is the ratio of velocity to time, and hence the dimensions of acceleration are 1 in length and -2 in time.

D

If ϕ is 0°, that is, if we are dealing with equatorial regions, cos 2ϕ is 1, and g is 978·032. If ϕ is 45°, cos 2ϕ is 0, and g is 980·621. If ϕ is 90°, that is, if we are considering polar regions, cos 2ϕ is − 1, and g is 983·210. We shall see later that the variation of gravity on some of the other planets is considerably greater than it is on the earth.

Velocity of Escape

If a body falls from a very great distance towards a planet or star, owing to the attraction of the planet or star on this body, and started from rest, there is a simple formula for finding the velocity with which it will reach the surface of the attracting body. If g is the value of gravity at the surface of the body and R is its radius, the velocity v with which the attracted body reaches the surface is

$$v = \sqrt{2gR}$$

Conversely, if a body is ejected from a planet or star with the velocity found from the above equation, it will go off into the depths of space, the planet or star losing control of it. (See Appendix IV.)

In the case of the earth g is 981, taking the average value, and R is 638×10^6, if the equatorial radius is used ; it makes very little difference which radius is taken. Hence $v = \sqrt{125 \times 10^{10}} = 112 \times 10^4$ cm./sec., or 11·2 kilometres per second, which is about 7 miles per second. Hence if a body is fired from the earth with the above or a greater velocity, it will not return but will go off into space and perhaps at some time it will be captured by a far-off star. Each body, planet or star, has its own *velocity of escape*, as this velocity is called, and we shall see later, in dealing with some of the planets, how important it is, especially in connection with the preservation or otherwise of an atmosphere.

Before leaving this subject something should be said about the method of computing the value of gravity on other bodies. This can be easily done provided the mass and diameter of the body are known, because the value of gravity on the surface of a body varies as its mass and inversely as the square of its radius. This is simply the universal law of gravitation extended to the attraction of a body on matter on its surface. As an application of this rule, take the case of the planet Mars. Its mass is 0·108 that of the earth and its diameter is 0·530 that of the earth. Hence gravity on Mars is $0·108/(0·530)^2 = 0·38$ the gravity on the earth's surface, or 373 cm./sec.

The Earth's Atmosphere

In certain respects atmospheric phenomena belong to the province of the meteorologist rather than to that of the astronomer, and we shall deal only with a few points regarding the atmosphere which have some direct bearing on the astronomer's work. From luminous meteors, which frequently appear as high as 70 miles, and occasionally even at 100 miles, we know that there must be some atmosphere in these regions. (The method by which these figures are known is given in Appendix V.) Aurorae have been observed at heights of 500 miles above the earth's surface and it is possible that the atmosphere extends beyond this,

though it must be in an extremely attenuated condition. The molecules of the atmosphere, like those of all gases, are in continual motion, their speeds increasing as the temperature rises. Collisions are always occurring between the molecules, but in a rarefied gas the collisions are relatively less frequent and a molecule has, on the average, a longer path before striking another molecule. There is an important relation between the molecular weight, m, of a gas, its *average* molecular velocity, v, and its absolute temperature, T. This relation is expressed in the form

$$v^2 \text{ varies as } T/m.$$

Nitrogen molecules have a velocity of 0·49 km./sec. at a temperature of 0° C., and as hydrogen has a molecular weight 1/14 that of nitrogen, the molecular velocity of hydrogen is $\sqrt{14} = 3·74$ times that of nitrogen, or 1·83 km./sec. If the temperature increases to 100° C., so that T is 373° K., instead of 273° K., the velocity of either gas increases in the ratio $\sqrt{373/273} = \sqrt{1·37} = 1·17$, so that the velocity of nitrogen and hydrogen molecules in this case would be 0·57 km./sec. and 2·14 km./sec., respectively. From these figures we can see that small planets in which the velocity of escape is low can easily lose some of or even all their atmosphere, more especially if their temperatures are high.

Refraction Caused by the Atmosphere

Most people have observed the phenomenon of the refraction of light. When a ray of light passes from a rarer into a denser medium its direction is altered in such a way that it approaches the perpendicular to the boundary between the media. Thus, if a ray of light passes from air into glass, it is bent as shown in Fig. 14. If, however, the ray of light enters the second medium at right angles to its surface, there is no bending or *refraction*—the name given to this bending or deviation of light.

If a ray of light from a celestial body reaches the earth it must pass through layers of the atmosphere which are increasing in density as they are closer to the surface of the earth. (Fig. 15.) Hence the atmosphere can be regarded as the denser medium, and the ray is continuously bent towards the perpendicular, so when it reaches the observer's eye it will appear to emanate from a point higher than it would if there were no atmosphere. If a star is in the zenith there is no refraction, but when it is close to the horizon the effect of refraction is at its maximum. Bodies near the horizon appear to be elevated by more than half a degree, and hence the sun, which subtends an angle of about half a degree at any point on the earth, is seen rising before any part of it is above the horizon. When the sun is just below the horizon, it is still visible owing to the same effect. These remarks apply also to the moon. Since refraction is greater close to the horizon than it is at higher elevations, the bottom of the disks of the sun and moon are raised more than the top when these bodies are rising or setting. This explains the apparently flattened appearance of the sun and moon on such occasions. The effect of refraction on stars is such that the astronomer must allow for it when he is engaged in accurate work. There are formulæ and tables supplying the amount of refraction for different elevations. Refraction varies for different temperatures and barometric heights, and these can be allowed for in the formulæ used for computing the effects of refraction.

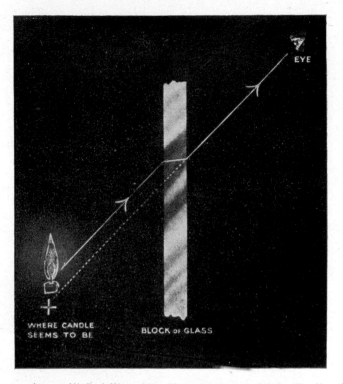

Fig. 14. A ray of light falling obliquely on a piece of glass has its direction altered, the ray being bent or refracted in such a manner that its new direction makes a smaller angle with the normal to the piece of glass. When it emerges from the glass into the rarer medium—the air—it is bent away from the normal. The effect produced on a ray of light passing from a rare to a denser medium—bent towards the normal—is important in connection with atmospheric refraction.

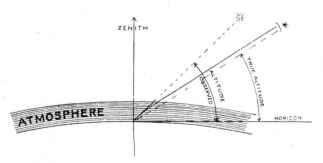

Fig. 15. Light from a star or any heavenly body passes through strata of the atmosphere which gradually increase in density. For this reason the ray is bent towards the normal to the layer at any point and the ray is thus bent downwards towards the earth. This causes the object to appear higher than it actually is.

One well-known effect of refraction is seen in the twinkling of the stars. If the atmosphere were at rest and the temperature constant this phenomenon would not occur, but vertical currents and horizontal movements in the layers of the atmosphere, changes in temperature and in pressure also, and even alterations in the amount of water vapour, are continually taking place. The result is that the index of refraction changes rapidly and hence the rays from a star alter their direction every instant. While the amount of this alteration is very small, it is nevertheless sufficient to convey the impression to an observer that the star is changing its position slightly, or twinkling. Stars near the horizon twinkle most, the reasons for which are obvious. In addition to twinkling, changes of colour are sometimes seen, and these are due to dispersion, or the difference of the deviations of the colours of the light from the star. All colours are not refracted by the same amount, violet rays being the most refrangible and red the least so.

Although twinkling of stars is a very common phenomenon, twinkling is not general in the case of the planets or the sun and moon. Stars are so far away from us that they present no visible disk* even in the most powerful telescope, and indeed the better the telescope the smaller the point of light a star appears when viewed through it. The planets, being comparatively near us, have sensible disks, and though refraction occurs just as with the stars, the rays from various parts of the disk follow different paths through the atmosphere, and there is no synchronization, the effects cancelling out. For this reason if there is any doubt about the nature of an unknown object, that is, whether it is a star or a planet, the matter can be settled by noticing whether it twinkles.

Steadiness of the air is an important consideration in selecting the site for an observatory, and of course an elevation that will exclude fog and dust, as far as this is possible, is also very important. At many observatories, in spite of every precaution, seeing conditions at times are not satisfactory. The clear, steady air at Flagstaff Observatory, Arizona, makes it the leading observatory for seeing conditions. If you ever look at a planet with a telescope, and you are concentrating your attention on some particular feature, the twinkling effect may be seen in the blurred details in the magnified image. Some of the American observatories, with their more ideal atmospheric conditions than we possess in these islands, have been able to carry out better planetary work than could ever be done by British astronomers. In spite of the ideal conditions, however, incorrects conclusions have sometimes been arrived at, as in the case of Mars (see p. 86).

(see p. 86).

CHAPTER IV

THE MOON

The Moon in Mythology

THE EARTH IS ACCOMPANIED IN ITS CIRCUIT ROUND THE SUN BY THE moon which is our nearest neighbour. Next to the sun, the moon is the most conspicuous of the heavenly bodies, and this is due, not to her size, but to her proximity to the earth. The average distance of the moon from

*This is not strictly true, as will be seen in the description of the interferometer in Chapter XI.

the earth is less than 240,000 miles—a very small distance astronomically considered. Many people know the moon only by her soft, silvery light which has made an irresistible appeal to countless generations, and which is such a boon to us, especially in the winter months, but they have never observed her rugged surface through an optical instrument, not even binoculars. The ancients were aware, just as we are, of the wonderful beauty of the lunar light, and the story of Selene in Greek mythology shows us that they regarded her as a very beautiful object.

Selene, the moon-goddess, loved to visit Mount Latmus, and indeed the mountain was supposed to belong to her. Her influence there made everything very quiet and beautiful. She found Endymion asleep there, leaving his sheep and goats untended, and night after night she returned, only to find the beautiful shepherd asleep. She knew that the air of her mountain had made him beautiful and also heedless, so she stayed by his flocks and watched them herself. One morning when she returned to the sky she looked very pale after her night's vigil, and when Jupiter asked her where she had been, she confessed that she had been guarding the sheep of the beautiful shepherd, and begged Jupiter not to allow Endymion to grow old like other mortals, but to look always as he did in his sleep. Jupiter replied that even the gods were unable to give everlasting youth and beauty to mortals without also giving them everlasting sleep, and so he decreed that Endymion should sleep for ever and should also be for ever young. Endymion still sleeps on Mount Latmus, and its wondrous beauty is even now a joy to all who climb its heights.

Lunar Features

The opportunity should not be missed of looking at the moon through a telescope—even a small telescope will suffice to show her wonderful beauty. Her plains and rugged mountain ranges and—most beautiful of all—her thousands of craters, have never failed to elicit exclamations of wonder from the novice who has not seen her before under such conditions. It is better to look at her from the time when she is a few days old up to a few days before full moon, rather than at full, to see many of her features, especially the craters, at their best. More than 30,000 craters have been mapped by selenographers (those who specialize on the study of the moon, from Selene the moon-goddess), and they are of various sizes, their diameters varying from 150 miles to less than quarter of a mile.

There are various theories regarding the origin of the lunar craters, and objections have been raised against all of them. One theory is that there was once volcanic activity on the moon, but on a very much larger scale than we have ever experienced on our planet, and hence the enormous sizes of many of the craters compared with terrestrial craters. Another theory is that they are due to bombardment by large meteorites—some of these several miles in diameter. An object this size, striking the moon's surface with a high velocity, say 30 miles a second or more, would produce an effect almost similar to that of a bomb. It would not make a hole a few miles wide but, owing to its enormous energy of motion, which would be converted into heat on impact, results like an explosion would occur and an enormous crater—perhaps a hundred miles in diameter—would be formed. Other theories have been suggested, but the subject is too long for discussion in a general work like the present.

The Moon's Phases

The moon's phases can be easily explained by reference to the diagram (see Fig. 16). On first appearance it seems that at new moon there should be an eclipse of the sun (the sun is supposed to be a long way off towards the top of the page), as the moon apparently intervenes directly between the earth and the sun. Also, at full moon one

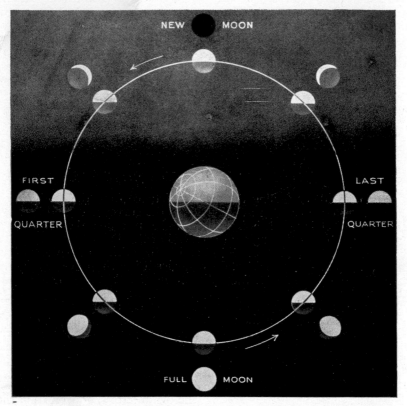

Fig. 16. The moon shines by sunlight reflected from her surface, the sun (supposed to be far away towards the top of the diagram) being responsible for the light. At full moon the whole illuminated side is turned towards the earth, and at new moon we are able to see only a small portion of the illuminated surface because most of it is turned away from us. Intermediate phases are shown in the diagram. The inner circle shows the condition of affairs as seen by an observer on a line drawn through the sun at right angles to the ecliptic, and the outer circle shows how the moon appears as viewed from the earth.

might surmise that the shadow of the earth would be cast on the moon, thus causing a lunar eclipse. This would take place at new and full moon every month if the moon moved in the plane of the ecliptic, but her orbit is inclined to this plane by more than 5°, and hence the sun, moon, and earth are not in a straight line at every new or full moon.

The phases of the moon are due to her revolution round the earth in a period of 27 days 7·72 hours. The expression 'revolution round the

earth' is a little misleading, because we want to know what part of the earth is the focus of the ellipse that the moon describes (see Introduction and Appendix I). Like all the planets, which move in elliptic orbits round the sun, the moon also moves in an elliptic orbit round the earth, but not round the centre of the earth. The mass of the moon is $1/81$ that of the earth, and as her mean distance from us is about 240,000 miles, the centre of gravity of the earth-moon system lies $240,000/81$ or about 3,000 miles from the earth's centre. This point is called the *barycentre*, and it is the point about which both earth and moon revolve, completing their revolution in about $27\frac{1}{3}$ days. It will be seen that not only does the moon revolve round the barycentre—a point a thousand miles below the surface of the earth—but the earth itself also revolves round the same point. This point is not fixed in the earth but alters its position every instant as the moon sweeps on in her orbit. Here we have another motion of the earth in addition to its orbital revolution round the sun and its axial rotation, to say nothing of its precessional motion described in the last chapter. All this shows the complications which arise in many of the astronomer's computations and how many different factors must be dealt with if he is to secure reliable results.

Measuring the Distance of the Moon from the Earth

The method for finding the moon's distance from the earth is the same in principle as the method used by the surveyor to find how far away an object is which is inaccessible. He measures the length of a base line and takes the angles at each end of this line between the lines drawn from either end to the object and to the other landmark marking the base. By securing a base and two angles it is a simple calculation to solve the triangle and to find the distance of the object from either end of the base line.

In the case of the moon it is necessary to use as long a base line as possible, and hence positions are selected, one in either hemisphere, to ensure a good base line. The diagram, Fig. 17, explains the procedure, and very accurate results have been obtained in this way. Of course, the distances measured by the method refer to the observatories, and, as the moon is very close to us, in comparison with other celestial bodies, her distance is not the same if measurements are made to different places on the earth's surface. For this reason the distance of the moon from the earth always refers to the distance between the centres of the two bodies, unless something to the contrary is stated. It is sometimes necessary to find how far away the moon is from a definite place on the earth's surface, and this is not a very difficult problem, knowing her distance from the earth's centre.

Knowing the distance to the moon, it is very easy to find her diameter. If someone at the centre of a circle wishes to know the length of any arc, it is only necessary for him to measure the angle which this arc subtends at the centre of the circle, and then, having measured the radius, he can find the length of the arc. Conversely, if he knows the length of the arc, he can find the length of the radius. The rules given for these calculations are as follows :

Multiply the radius by the number of seconds subtended by the arc and divide the result by 206,265. This will give the length of the arc.

If the length of the arc is known and that of the radius is required, multiply the length of the arc by 206,265, and divide the result by the number of seconds in the angle. This will give the radius. This rule can be applied to a line provided that the angle subtended by it is small and also that the line is perpendicular to the line of sight. Thus, if a line which is known to be 10 feet in length subtends an angle of 20 minutes (1,200 seconds) at the position of an observer, and it is required to know its distance, we multiply 10 by 206,265 and divide by 1,200, obtaining 1,719 feet as the distance. This assumes that the line does not slant in either direction but is at right angles to the line drawn from the observer

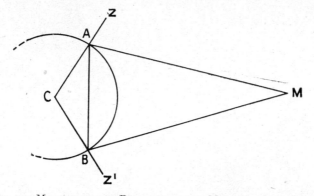

FIG. 17. MEASURING THE DISTANCE OF THE MOON FROM THE EARTH
A and B represent two observatories, which will be assumed to be on the same meridian, and to be separated as far as possible, one in the northern and the other in the southern hemisphere. The zenith distance of the moon M is measured at each observatory, or the zenith distance of some prominent lunar landmark, say, a mountain. These zenith distances are the angles MAZ and MBZ', and from these the angles MAC and MBC are known, being the supplements of the zenith distances. Knowing the angles CAB and CBA and the distance AB, derived from the latitudes of the observatories, the angles MAB and MBA and the side AB in the triangle MAB enable the distances AM and BM to be found.

to its middle point, or, as the line is so short, to any point in it. The line can be regarded as an arc of a circle of very large radius when the angle is small.

When we look at the moon we can regard her diameter as an arc of a very large circle of which a place on the earth is centre, and the rule can be applied with safety, because the angle subtended by the moon at the earth is small—a little over half a degree. It has been found that the angle subtended by the moon at the earth is not always the same and this proves that her orbit is not circular but elliptical. The greatest and least distances of the moon from the earth (measured from centre to centre of each body) are 252,710 miles and 225,463 miles, and her diameter is 2,160 miles. The angles subtended at these distances are 29·38′ and 32·97′, the mean being 31·08′.

Mass of the Moon

It is much more difficult to weigh the moon, although she is so close to us, than it is to weigh the planets which have satellites. We shall show

later how simple the latter process is. One method used to weigh the moon is to compute the amount of precession and nutation for various masses of the moon, and then, knowing from observation the amount of precession and nutation, the mass of the moon which satisfies these results is found. Another method depends on the varying position of the barycentre, which, as we have seen, lies about 1,000 miles below the earth's surface. We know that it is at this depth because the mass of the moon was assumed, but suppose we found from *observation* that the barycentre lay at this depth, obviously we could then easily compute the mass of the moon in comparison with that of the earth.

If there were no moon the centre of the earth would describe an ellipse in its orbital motion round the sun. Perhaps it would be more correct to say that the sun and earth would describe ellipses each round their common centre of gravity, but as the sun weighs about 330,000 times as much as the earth, the centre of gravity of the two bodies is only 300 miles from the sun's centre. This is so small in comparison with the sun's radius that the sun's centre can be taken as the focus of the ellipse described by the earth. Hence, it is possible to compute the earth's position with great accuracy as it moves round the sun, assuming that there is no disturbing body, and, knowing the position of the earth, the sun's positions, as seen from the earth, can also be found very accurately.

The diagram, Fig. 18, shows that the movement of the barycentre (i.e., the centre of the earth-moon system as explained) round the centre of the sun as the focus implies certain irregularities in the motion of the earth and hence in the motion of the sun as seen from the earth. Sometimes the sun is displaced (apparently) so that he is ahead of, and at other times he is behind, his place predicted on the assumption that the earth's centre is describing the ellipse. In this way it has been found possible to compute the distance of the barycentre from the centre of the earth, and hence the moon's mass. The moon's mass is now taken to be 0·0123 or 1/81 of the earth's mass, so that the mass of the moon is about $7·35 \times 10^{25}$ grams.

Moon's Density, Surface Gravity, and Velocity of Escape

Knowing the moon's mass and volume, the latter computed from its diameter, its density is easily found. This is 3·34, which is 0·6 of the earth's density. Surface gravity, as we have seen in Chapter III, varies as the mass and inversely as the square of the radius. The radius of the moon is 0·272 that of the earth's radius, and hence surface gravity on the moon is $0·0123/(0·272)^2 = 0·166$ that on the earth's surface. The velocity of escape varies as $\sqrt{gR}$ (see page 50), and hence on the surface of the moon the velocity of escape is $\sqrt{0·166 \times 0·272}$ times the velocity of escape on the earth's surface, or 0·214. As on the earth velocity of escape is nearly 7 miles a second, that on the moon is 1·5 miles a second. Hence bodies on the moon would not only weigh less than they do on the earth, if tested by a spring balance, a pound weight on the earth weighing about one-sixth of this on the moon, but also bodies projected on the moon would have a much greater range than they have on the earth. On the earth a body thrown vertically with a velocity of 96 feet a second would reach a height of 144 feet, but on the moon it would rise to six times this height before falling back.

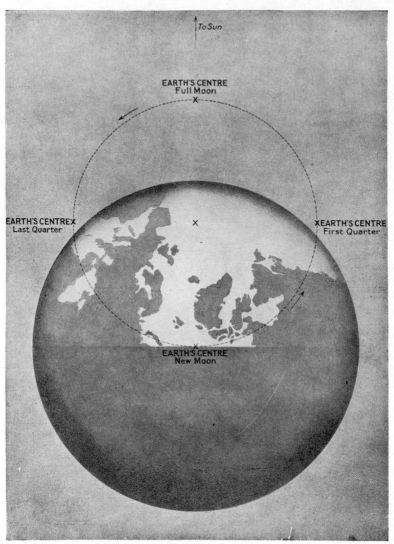

Fig. 18. The earth's centre revolves round the barycentre—a point about 3,000 miles from the centre of the earth or 1,000 miles below its surface. Its position depends on the ratio of the masses of the moon and earth At full moon the earth's centre is nearer to the sun than its barycentre by 3,000 miles, and at new moon, when the moon is between the earth and the sun, the earth's centre is 3,000 miles farther from the sun than the barycentre. The positions of the sun, measured from observatories on the earth's surface, are referred to the centre of the earth, not to its barycentre. As the radius of the earth subtends an angle of 8·8 seconds of arc at the distance of the sun, a length of 3,000 miles would subtend an arc of about six and a half seconds. For this reason the sun appears to be six and a half seconds of arc in front of its average place at the moon's first quarter and the same amount behind the average place at the last quarter. By measuring this angle accurately it is then easy to find the ratio of the mass of the moon to that of the earth.

The Moon is Devoid of an Atmosphere

The comparatively low velocity of escape suggests that if ever the moon had an atmosphere she would be more likely to lose it than the earth would. We know for certain that the moon has no atmosphere now, but this does not prove that she never had an atmosphere. When a star is occulted by the moon, in other words, when the moon during her motion round the earth interposes between a star and an observer on the earth, the star disappears suddenly without any preliminary fading. If the moon had an atmosphere this would not occur as some of the starlight would be refracted and also scattered when the star had gone behind the moon, so that we might describe the disappearance under such conditions as a gradual fade out. In addition, the exact instant of an occultation can be computed and also the exact instant of reappearance when the star emerges from behind the moon, and these correspond to the times given by observation, unaltered by refraction. During a solar eclipse no effect has been noticed which could be ascribed to the atmosphere of the moon, which is then between the earth and the sun.

Although the moon has no atmosphere at present there may have been a time when her atmosphere was considerable, but the lighter gases would be likely to escape fairly rapidly from her surface. We have seen that the velocity of the hydrogen molecules at 0° C. is 1·83 km./sec., or about 1·14 miles per second, which is a little less than the velocity of escape for the moon. It seems, therefore, that the moon would not lose even her hydrogen and a fortiori she would not lose the denser gases at 0° C. The time factor is important, however, as the following figures given by Sir James Jeans inform us.

Jeans has calculated that the time required for the entire isothermal* region of a planet's atmosphere to escape into space is about a thousand years, if the mean velocity of the molecules is one-fourth the velocity of escape. In the case of the moon the mean velocity of even the nitrogen molecules —nearly 0·5 km./sec. at 0° C.—is greater than one-fourth the velocity of escape on the surface of the moon, and, therefore, the moon could not have retained any atmosphere for a long time. If the fraction is one-fifth instead of one-fourth, the time increases enormously and is about a thousand million years. In the case of the earth, one-fifth of the velocity of escape is 2·2 km./sec., and we have seen that the mean velocity of the hydrogen molecules at 100° C. is 2·14 km./sec. When the temperature of the earth was much higher in the past than it is now it seems very probable that it lost its hydrogen, and in the case of the moon, one can affirm with a fair degree of certainty that she lost all her gases very quickly.

The Moon and the Tides

The connection of the tides with the moon is very obvious to those who live at the seaside. Each day the tides rise on average 51 minutes later, and this period corresponds with the average amount by which the moon is later each day in crossing the meridian at any place. That the sun also has some influence on the tides is clear from the fact that very high and very low tides are associated with the relative positions of the

---

* Isothermal means an equal degree of heat, from the Greek *isos*, equal, and *thermos*, heat.

sun and moon with regard to the earth, high tides occurring when the
moon is near full or new, and low tides being experienced at quarter phases.
Although the mathematical analysis of the cause of the tides is slightly
involved, it is possible to give a tentative explanation without much
mathematics. Those who wish to see a further investigation of the subject
are referred to Appendix VI.

We have already seen that the attraction between two bodies varies
as the product of their masses and inversely as the square of their
distance apart. Dealing with the earth and moon only, it is obvious that,
since the mass of the moon does not change, her attraction on a portion
of the earth nearest to her is greater than her attraction on the more
remote parts. Hence the attraction of the moon on any part of the earth
turned towards her is greater than her attraction on an equal mass at
the distance of the earth's centre, and also her attraction on the latter is
greater than it is on a similar mass on the other side of the earth. It is
the *difference* between the moon's pull on the waters near to her and her
pull on the earth as a whole that causes high tide on one side of the earth,
and it is also the *difference* between her pull on the earth as a whole, and
her pull on the waters on the other side of the earth, which is less than her
pull on the earth as a whole, that causes high tides on this opposite side
as well. This seems a remarkable anomaly, but readers may accept it as a
fact at present. The old explanation that was often given was that the
moon pulled the earth away from the waters on the far side and left them
behind, thus causing high tide on the other side of the earth—an explanation which probably puzzled many people. Their confusion was not
decreased when they were told that the sun had a similar effect, so at
the same time the sun and moon were pulling the earth away from the
waters and leaving them behind, even at places very far apart on the
earth's surface. While this is partly true its statement in this form is
certainly misleading.

The moon's attractive force on a point on the surface of the earth is
easily found, knowing her mass and distance. Apply the rule about the
attraction varying as the product of the masses and inversely as the
square of the distance, and from this the moon's attraction for any mass,
say 1lb., on the earth, can be determined.

Let M_e and M_m be the masses of the earth and moon respectively,
and let the distance of any given mass—say 1lb.—from the centres of
the earth and moon be d_e and d_m. The attraction of the earth on this
mass is proportional to $M_e \times 1/d_e^2$, and that of the moon is proportional
to $M_m \times 1/d_m^2$. The ratio of the attraction of the earth to that of the
moon is, therefore, $\dfrac{M_e d_m^2}{M_m d_e^2}$ or $81 \times \left(\dfrac{d_m}{d_e}\right)^2$. Instead of using the separate

values of d_e and d_m it will be sufficient to use the ratio in all cases.

Now suppose that this ratio is 60 ; the above will supply us with the
pull of the moon on 1 lb. weight at the distance of the moon from the
earth's centre, and if the ratio is 59 it will supply us with this value when
the weight of 1 lb. is on the side of the earth nearest to the moon. By
varying this ratio it is possible to find how much the moon pulls the
weight on different portions of the earth's surface. If the ratio is 60
the earth's pull is $81 \times 60^2 = 291,600$ times that of the moon, or taking the
reciprocal of this number, the moon's pull is 0·000003429 lb. It is assumed
that the moon is in the zenith at the time, to simplify the problem, and

her lifting force on 1 lb. is then 0·000003429 lb. This is not the force exercised by the moon in lifting the water ; the effective force in producing tides is the *difference* between the attraction on the water and that on the earth as a whole.

Now consider the distance of an object on the earth nearest to the moon, when the moon is in the zenith. In this case d_m/d_e is not 60 but 59, and if the object were on the other side of the earth the ratio would be 61. Hence the earth's attraction is now $81 \times 59^2 = 281{,}961$ times the moon's attraction, or the attraction of the moon on 1 lb. is 0·000003547 lb., and the difference between this and the attraction on 1 lb. if placed as far from the moon as the earth's centre is 0·000000118 lb. This is the tide-raising force tending to move 1 lb. of water away from the surface of the earth.

On the other side of the earth where d_m/d_e is 61, the earth's attraction is $81 \times 61^2 = 301{,}401$ times that of the moon, and hence the moon's attraction on 1 lb. on the opposite side is 0·000003318 lb., the difference between this and the attraction on 1 lb. if placed as far away as the earth's centre, being 0·000000111 lb. In this case the attraction on the far side is *less* than that on the centre, and it is this difference of 111 in 100 million that is responsible for the tide on the far side, just as it is the difference of 118 in 100 million that is responsible for high tide on the near side to the moon. It will be seen that the tide-raising force is only about one-thirtieth of the moon's attraction.

The above reasoning will show that tides should be higher when the moon is near the earth and vice versa, and this is just what happens. In fact the tides would be about 20 per cent higher and lower than the mean when the moon is in perigee and apogee (nearest to and at greatest distances from the earth) if the sun did not interfere. As a matter of interest the results will be worked out on the basis of the above reasoning.

When the moon is at apogee—252,710 miles from the earth—this distance is 63·74 times the earth's radius. Multiplying the square of this by 81 the result is 329,086, and the reciprocal of this is 0·000003039. On the side of the earth then nearest to the moon, the distance of the ocean, assuming that the moon is in the zenith, is 62·74 times the earth's radius, and when the square of this is multiplied by 81 the result is 318,840, the reciprocal of which is 0·000003136. The difference between the attraction in this latter case and that at a distance of the earth's centre is, therefore, 0·000000097. Hence the moon's tide-raising force when the moon is in apogee compared with that when she is at the mean distance is in the ratio 97 to 118, or in other words, there would be a decrease of 21 in 118 or just under 20 per cent. In the same way it can be shown that at perigee the increase would be about 20 per cent provided the sun did not interfere.

The explanation just given might lead readers to infer that high water is always under or nearly under the moon, and this would take place under ideal conditions, but these do not exist. If a tidal wave started by the moon could run round the oceans at the same rate as the moon seems to go round, high tide would be under the moon, but the oceans are not sufficiently deep for this. In addition, there are many obstructions in the form of continents and islands which would prevent the crest of the tidal wave keeping pace with the moon even under ideal conditions. The

velocity of a wave which is moving freely depends on the depth of the water and also on gravity. The formula for finding the velocity, v, is :

$$v = \sqrt{gd}$$

g, d and v being expressed in the same units.

In equatorial regions the ocean is moving with a velocity of about 1,038 miles an hour (in space, not relative to the earth) owing to the earth's rotation. As the moon is revolving round the earth in the same direction in which the earth rotates, her apparent velocity relative to a point in the ocean is less than the above figures by about 4 per cent, so we may assume a velocity of 1,000 miles an hour to be necessary in our ideal ocean for the tidal wave to keep pace with the moon, or 1,467 feet a second. Substituting 32 for g in the above equation, $1,467 = \sqrt{32\,d}$, or $32\,d = 2,152,089$, from which $d = 67,253$ feet or 12·7 miles.

If the ocean were about 13 miles deep, we should, therefore, have high tide under the moon, provided there were no obstructions in the form of masses of land. As the ocean is nowhere so deep as this, there is a lag of the tidal wave, though there is a fairly definite interval between the time of the moon's passage over the meridian anywhere and the time of the next high tide. The 'establishment of a port' or 'the mean high water interval' —a more correct term—is the average interval between the passage of the moon across the meridian of a port and the next high tide. At New York this establishment is over 8 hours and in London it is under 2 hours. The sizes of tides vary throughout the month, not only because of the positions of the sun and moon, as already described, but also owing to meteorological factors, such as wind and even barometric pressure, the height of the tide increasing when the barometer falls. A rough rule to remember is that a fall of one inch in the barometer corresponds to a rise of about one foot in water-level.

If, as may happen, a tidal wave arrives at a given place by different routes the result may be a double high water, the second an hour or so later than the first. One of the best known examples of this phenomenon is at Southampton and the nearby coast as far as Poole where there are double high waters twice in rather more than twelve hours. The practical effect is that the high water lasts longer than it would otherwise though the second is a little lower than the first. Another incidental effect is that there is less time for the ebb than for the flood so that the former flows much more rapidly.

The explanation that used to be given was that the tidal wave came up the Channel, divided at the Needles and reached Southampton direct up the Solent and then a little later round Spithead. This explanation is now known to be false. The actual explanation in detail is much too abstruse to be given here, but it was investigated by Lord Kelvin and Sir George Darwin and is given in *Admiralty Manual of Tides*, by A. T. Doodson and H. D. Warburg (pages 218 and 223–226).

The Moon Affects the Tides more than the Sun

The sun's effect in causing tides is less than that of the moon, and the following simple investigation will show how their relative effects are computed.

It may be assumed that the mass of the sun is 333,434* times that of the earth and that the sun's mean distance from the earth is 23,464 times the earth's radius. The attraction of the sun on 1 lb. at the distance of the earth's centre is 333,434/23,464^2 lb., which is 0·00060562751 lb. If now we consider the sun's attraction on the same weight on the side of the earth nearest to the sun, instead of 23,464 we must use 23,463, and on computing the value of the attraction in this case it comes out as 0·00060567919 lb. We have seen that the moon's attraction on 1 lb. at a distance equal to that separating the centres of the earth and moon is 0·000003429 lb., and hence the sun's attraction at the same distance is about 177 times that of the moon. This does not imply that the sun's tide-generating force is 177 times the moon's because, as previously shown, we are dealing with *differences,* and the difference between the

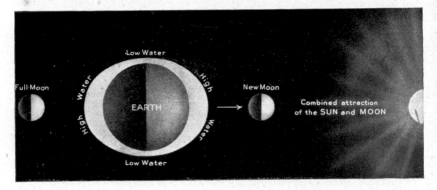

FIG. 19. CAUSES OF SPRING TIDES

It is assumed, to simplify the problem, that the sun and moon each produce high tides at the point of the earth nearest to them and also at the opposite point. When the sun, earth and moon are in a line, which happens at new and full moon, the combined pulls of the sun and moon produce the Spring Tides. When the moon is in quadrature (90° from the sun) the pulls partly neutralize each other, that of the moon being the greater, and Neap Tides then occur.

sun's attraction on 1 lb. on the earth's surface nearest the sun and 1 lb. as far from the sun as the centre of the earth is 0·00060567919 minus 0·00060562751, or 0·0000005168. We have seen that the corresponding figures for the moon are 0·000000118, and hence the ratio of the sun's tide-generating force to that of the moon is as 51·7 to 118 or as 1 to 2·28. We can say, therefore, that the sun's tide-generating force is about 5/11 that of the moon. This explains why spring tides—tides occurring at or close to new or full moon—are so much higher than the average tides, while neap tides—those occurring at or near the moon's quarters—are much lower than the average. In the former case the sun and moon are acting in the same line and in the latter case each is forming its own tide at places on the surface of the earth about 90° apart. (See Fig. 19.)

A phenomenon noticed by those living at the seaside is the recurrence of high tide at the same hour at the same place when the moon is full or new, and also at the quarters the moon gives high water at the same time

* The method for finding the sun's mass will be shown in the next chapter.

of the day. To explain the reason for this, it will suffice to consider one case—say full moon.

When the moon is full she is in a line with the sun and earth and hence, regarded from the earth, is in the opposite part of the heavens from the sun. Now the sun crosses the meridian each day about noon and also crosses the meridian again about midnight, though we are unable to see the sun then, unless we are north of the Arctic Circle. In the first case the moon is nearly due north, close to the meridian. When the sun crosses the meridian about midnight we should expect the moon to be on or near the meridian looking south, and this will take place each month, irrespective of the place. The establishment of the port enables us to say how long after the moon crosses the meridian high tide will occur, and this is usually very regular, although high winds may alter it to some extent, but we need not deal with local circumstances. It is not surprising, therefore, that high tide should occur about the same hour month by month at full moon, and the same argument can be applied to the other phases of the moon.

Effects of Tidal Friction

In the open ocean the amount of tidal friction is small because the water is not moving laterally, although there is a lateral movement of the wave. In the shallow seas there is a considerable amount of lateral movement which is responsible for friction and as a consequence, a slight slowing down of the rotation of the earth. Amongst the seas that exercise most influence in this way may be mentioned the Bering Sea, Fox Strait, the English Channel, the Yellow Sea, Malacca Strait, the North Sea and the Irish Sea. It has been estimated that the day has lengthened by about one second in the last 120,000 years, and, while tidal friction is a slow process, yet in the course of the geological ages it has made a considerable difference to the length of the day. Tidal friction has been responsible for the phenomenon known to exist in certain satellites—our own included—and almost certainly in some of the planets, the equality of the period of revolution round their primaries and their time of axial rotation. The moon rotates in the same period as she revolves round the earth and hence we never see her other side, though we see more than half of her total surface. Owing to the elliptic orbit which the moon describes round the earth her orbital motion is not quite uniform, though her axial rotation is uniform, and hence there is an *apparent* rocking of the moon from side to side, which is known as her libration in longitude. In addition, the moon's axis is inclined at an angle of about $6\frac{1}{2}°$ with reference to a perpendicular to the plane of her orbit, and for this reason we are able to see $6\frac{1}{2}°$ beyond the pole that is tilted towards us and then, a fortnight later, we can see $6\frac{1}{2}°$ beyond the other pole. This effect is known as the moon's libration in latitude, and when the two librations are taken into account, it has been found that we can see 59 per cent of the moon's surface.

We see on the moon what will some day occur to our own planet—a very long day, which will be nearly fifty times as long as the present day. Tidal friction on the moon, the tides being caused by the earth, must have been very much greater than it is on the earth, as the more massive earth would have a greater effect in producing tides on the moon than the moon has on the earth. It is true that there are no oceans on the moon,

E

nor indeed is there water in any form, but there may have been in the past, and even if there had not been, tidal action in the molten interior of a satellite or planet cannot be ignored.

Tidal Friction and the Future of the Earth-Moon System

It has been estimated that in a period of 50,000 million years the earth's period of rotation will be 47 of our present days, and this will also be the period of the moon's revolution round the earth. As the earth's axial rotation slows down, the moon recedes from the earth, in accordance with the principle of the conservation of angular momentum (see page 160), and a simple calculation shows that if the moon's period of orbital revolution were 47 of our present days instead of $27\frac{1}{3}$, her mean distance from the earth would be more than 340,000 miles. At this stage, however, the solar tides will intervene to prevent the moon remaining permanently at this distance from the earth. The lunar tides will then be very much less than they are now—in fact the moon's tide-generating force at this distance would be about one-third of its present value—but the solar tides will be practically the same and hence more effective than the new lunar tides. The solar tides, continuing to operate on the earth, will still further lengthen its period of rotation, and this will react on the moon, causing her to approach the earth. The moon will continue to approach the earth until she comes within the 'Roche Limit,' when she will be broken up by the action of the earth. An explanation of the Roche Limit is given in the next chapter, and the reasons for the moon's recession and subsequent approach to the earth are set forth in Appendix VII.

Why the Moon Appears Enlarged near the Horizon

The apparent difference in the size of the moon, and the sun as well, at different times or when they are at different distances from the horizon, is a familiar phenomenon. When the full moon has just risen she looks larger than she does in an hour or two when she is well above the horizon. One explanation of this illusion is that we instinctively compare the moon with houses or trees, when she is not far from the horizon, but do not do so when she is high. We know these to be large objects, and hence interpret the impression made on the retina by the moon as due to something large. Another explanation is that we subconsciously think of the sky as a flattened dome, not a perfect hemisphere, and for this reason we interpret the high moon or noonday sun as nearer objects than when they are close to the horizon, and conversely, we think of the rising moon or sun as far off. When we think a thing is far away we also think of it as larger. For example, if we see a colt half a mile away and are assured that it is a mile off, we may interpret it as a horse or at least as much larger than we imagined it to be at first.

It must be admitted that neither of these explanations is very satisfactory, and recently Professor E. G. Boring and his associates at Harvard Psychological Laboratory undertook experiments with an artificial moon the size of which could be varied to appear to agree with the real moon. Compared with the artificial moon placed at a distance of twelve feet, the real moon appeared anywhere from two to six degrees in diameter (its angular diameter is about half a degree) to people with normal vision

using both eyes. The only theory which seemed feasible, though it was not finally accepted, was Ames' theory of ocular torsion. When the eyes are raised, the right eye tends to rotate clockwise, as seen from behind, with respect to the left eye. This may be an explanation of the illusion of the large moon for binocular vision. Congenitally monocular persons, who were uninfluenced by the knowledge of the illusion, did not perceive it during the experiments, but there is no indication as to the effect on persons who had lost the sight of an eye. Presumably they saw the illusion like those with normal eyes.

It is interesting to look at the full moon, when she is near the horizon, with averted vision—for instance—looking at her between the legs. In such circumstances the illusion is not so obvious and indeed may not be noticeable. While the results of experiments are not yet conclusive, it may be accepted that the first two explanations are extremely unsatisfactory and should be excised from astronomical textbooks.

CHAPTER V

THE PLANETS: GENERAL CONSIDERATIONS

MOST OF THIS CHAPTER MAY SEEM A DIGRESSION FROM THE CONSIDERATION of the physical features, atmosphere, sizes, densities, etc., of the individual planets. The subjects have been dealt with, however, so that detailed explanations of each separate planet can be obviated, and various matters relating to the planets can be exhibited in tabular form, thus assisting the reader when he wishes to refer to any particular heading. It is hoped that the brief outline given in this chapter will make clear the methods by which results have been attained. As the mass, size, density, mean distance from the sun, etc., are given in the table in Chapter VI it is unnecessary to repeat these in the text.

The Earth

The earth is one of the family of nine planets which belong to our solar system, and all of these share with it in describing elliptical orbits round the sun. It may be pointed out that there is no reason why a planet should not describe a circular orbit—and indeed Venus moves in an orbit which is nearly circular—but the probability of an orbit being an exact circle is so small that we may say it never occurs. An ellipse and a circle, together with a parabola and a hyperbola, are all possible forms of orbits, and, as we shall see later, all of them, except the circle, are found in the case of comets. If a body moves in a parabolic or hyperbolic orbit it finally passes away from the attractive force of the central body, because a parabola and a hyperbola are curves which are described as 'open,' that is, they do not close in on themselves like an ellipse or a circle. Sometimes a comet which is moving round the sun in a closed curve—an ellipse—is so disturbed by passing close to one of the larger planets that its elliptical orbit is turned into a hyperbolic orbit and it is lost for ever to the sun. We need not fear that this will happen to any of the planets because they do not approach one another close enough to produce great disturbances in one another's motion, or in other words, their mutual perturbations are not serious.

Kepler's Laws

Kepler's laws of planetary motion were not all announced at the same time. The first and second were announced in 1609, but the third was not discovered until ten years later, and all three were included in *The Harmony of the World*, published in 1619. These laws introduced considerable simplification into celestial mechanics, as epicycles and other curves were now abandoned (these were postulated by the ancient astronomers to explain planetary motions) and nature was shown to work on a much simpler plan than had been previously postulated. Kepler's laws are as follows :

1. The orbit of every planet is an ellipse with the sun at one of its foci.

2. Every planet revolves so that the line joining it to the sun sweeps over equal areas in equal intervals of time.

3. The squares of the periodic times of any two planets are in the same proportion as the cubes of their mean distances from the sun.

These laws are given before we proceed to deal with each planet separately because they explain how certain details about planets, in particular their distances from the sun and their orbital speeds, can be easily determined. It should be said that the first and third laws are easily deduced by a mathematical analysis on the assumption of the attraction of the sun varying inversely as the square of the distance of the planet, and as a result of this assumption it is shown that the orbit must be a circle, ellipse, parabola, or hyperbola, according to the initial conditions of motion.

We shall now show how to apply these laws for certain computations, and shall start first of all with the third law.

It should be noticed that the third law deals with *mean* distances, not with the maximum or minimum distances. The mean distance is, of course, the average or mean of the maximum and minimum distances of a planet, and we shall deal with it in every case.

The Synodic and Sidereal Periods of a Planet

If we could imagine an astronomer on the sun watching the motion of any planet, it is obvious that he could tell after a time how long it required to move round the sun. It would be necessary to notice how many degrees it moved in a certain time, say a year or more (according to the planet) with reference to the stars, and from this the astronomer could easily calculate how long it would require to move over 360°, that is, how long it would require to complete a revolution round the sun. If he lived sufficiently long he could watch the movements of planets as far out as Saturn or perhaps even Uranus, but his span of life would not allow observations of planets outside Uranus during their complete circuits. The name *sidereal period* is given to the time that a planet requires to revolve round the sun, but as an astronomer can never observe from the sun he must find the sidereal period by some other means.

When a planet is observed from the earth it will sometimes be in a line with the sun, and is then in *conjunction*. If the planet lies between the earth and the sun (Venus and Mercury are frequently in this position) it is said to be in *inferior conjunction*, and if the sun lies between the earth and the planet, which can occur with all the planets, it is said to be

in *superior conjunction*. A planet is in *opposition* when it is in a part of the heavens directly opposite the sun, viewed, of course, from the earth. The interval between two successive conjunctions or oppositions is called a planet's *synodic period*, and hence it refers to the apparent time that a planet requires to go round the sun, the earth being the astronomer's point of view. This period can be determined by observation and then the *sidereal period* can be easily deduced from it by a simple formula.

Suppose S is the synodic period of a planet as found from observation and E is the earth's sidereal period—the time that the earth requires to revolve round the sun. This time, if we could imagine an observer on the sun, would be judged by the return of the earth to the same position with reference to the stars, just like any other planet. It is actually the interval between successive returns of the sun to the same point among the stars. Let P be the corresponding sidereal period of the planet. Since the planet moves through 360° in a time P during its revolution round the sun, its angular velocity is proportional to $1/P$ because it moves through $360°/P$ in a unit of time. Similarly the earth's angular velocity is proportional to $1/E$. The angular velocity of the planet as *seen from the earth* must be the difference between the angular velocities of the planet and of the earth as seen from the sun, and as this angular velocity is proportional to $1/S$, we obtain the simple formula

$$\frac{1}{S} = \frac{1}{P} - \frac{1}{E}$$

for an *inferior* planet, that is, a planet with orbit inside the earth's orbit.

If the planet's orbit is outside that of the earth, in which case it is a *superior* planet, P is greater than E and $1/S$ would be negative, which is impossible. In this case it is only necessary to change the signs of the terms on the right hand side of the equation, so that

$$\frac{1}{S} = \frac{1}{E} - \frac{1}{P}$$

The sidereal period of any planet can, therefore, be determined from the formula

$$\frac{1}{P} = \frac{1}{E} \pm \frac{1}{S}$$

the plus sign being used if we are considering an inferior planet and the negative sign being used if it is a superior planet.

Take the case of Venus, an inferior planet with a synodic period of 583·92 days. Using the upper sign and substituting 365·25 for E, we obtain $1/P = 1/365\cdot25 + 1/583\cdot92 = 949\cdot17/213,277$. Hence $P = 224\cdot7$ days. If we are dealing with Mars, the synodic period of which is 779·94 days, the lower sign is used because Mars is a superior planet. In this case $1/P = 1/365\cdot25 - 1/779\cdot94 = 414\cdot69/284,873$. Hence $P = 686\cdot95$ days. All the other planets can be dealt with in the same manner.

Determination of a Planet's Mean Distance from the Sun

The third law deals not only with the *mean distance* but also with the periodic time, which is the same thing as the *sidereal period*, the determination of which has just been considered. If, therefore, we knew the

mean distance of any one planet, say, the earth, from the sun, we could find
the mean distance of any other planet, when we had computed its sidereal
period, expressing this distance in terms of the distance of the earth from
the sun as the unit. Generally it is easier to make the computations by
taking the year as the unit of time and the earth's mean distance from the
sun as the unit of distance.

As an example we shall find the mean distance of Mars from the sun,
assuming that its sidereal period is 686·95 days, or 1·881 years.

The third law can be expressed in the form $T^2 = a^3$, if T is the time
in years and a is the mean distance of the planet from the earth.   If
$T = 1·881$, $a^3 = 3·538161$ and $a = 1·524$. The mean distance of the earth
from the sun, known as an astronomical unit, is the unit in all cases of this
kind, and as it is 93,005,000 miles, this gives the mean distance of Mars
from the sun as 141,740,000 miles and the mean distances of all the
planets from the sun can be determined in the same manner.

Determination of the Sun's Distance and Diameter

The method described for finding the distance of the moon (see page 56)
could be used for finding the sun's distance also, but the results would not
be very accurate owing to the much greater distance of the sun from the
earth. The radius of the earth subtends an angle a little under 9 seconds
of arc at the sun's distance, and in dealing with such a small angle as this,
minute errors would be responsible for very large errors in the determination of the sun's distance. Suppose, for instance, that we adopt a
value 8·80 seconds for this angle, which is near the true figure, and apply
the rule given in the previous chapter, we find that the sun's distance
from the earth is (206,265 × 3,963·5)/8·8 = 92,901,000 miles. But if an
error of only 0·01 second occurs in determining the small angle, this
implies an error of 1 in 880 which would produce an error of more than
100,000 miles in computing the sun's distance.

It is scarcely necessary to remark that astronomers would not attempt
to find the sun's distance by *measuring* the angle subtended by the earth's
radius—a physical impossibility. A long base line on the earth's surface
would provide the necessary data if the angle subtended by such a base
line at the sun's distance were known, but it has been found convenient
to express the sun's distance in terms of the angle subtended by the earth's
equatorial radius, and of course the reduction from any base line to a base
line the length of the earth's radius is a simple calculation. The name
given to this angle is the *sun's parallax* (contrast this with the parallax
of a star as explained on page 116).

Instead of measuring the angle subtended at the sun by the method
already described in the case of the moon, it is obvious that much better
results would be obtained if the angle subtended at a nearer body could
be determined and the distance of this body calculated, provided the
relative distances of this body from the earth and the sun are known. The
planets Venus and Mars make much closer approaches to the earth than
the sun does and they have been used to find the sun's distance, but the
best determination has been accomplished by means of the minor planet
Eros (see page 71–2) which sometimes approaches the earth as closely
as 14 million miles. (See Fig. 20.) On such occasions its distance from the
earth is found by a method similar to that described for the moon, though,

of course, as it is at a much greater distance than the moon is, it is
not possible to find its distance from the earth with such accuracy as the
moon's distance is determined. From the period of Eros, its mean distance
from the sun is known, and from various other details, such as the time
when it makes its closest approach to the sun, the eccentricity of its orbit,
the inclination of the orbit to the ecliptic, etc., its distance from the earth
at any time can be computed, such distance being expressed in terms of

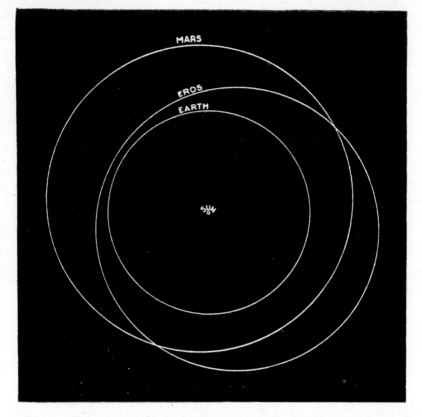

Fig. 20. The orbits of the earth, Mars and Eros, and the relatively close
approach of the orbits of Eros and the earth are shown. This minor planet
has been used to determine the distance of the earth from the sun.

the astronomical unit, whatever value that may have. This point should
be clearly understood. The major axis of the orbit of Eros, its distance
from the sun at any time and also the distance of the earth from the sun
and therefore from Eros at any time, are computed in terms of an astronomical unit, without making any assumptions regarding the *length* of
this unit. The possibility of this will be obvious from our previous
example relating to the mean distance of Mars. Knowing, then, the distance of Eros from the earth by such computations, in terms of an astronomical unit, and knowing the same distance in miles, measured by trigonometrical methods, it is easy to equate one with the other and to express

an astronomical unit in terms of miles. The most recent determination of the sun's distance was accomplished by Sir Harold S. Jones, the Astronomer Royal, who completed his investigations in 1941. The approach of Eros in 1930–1 to a distance of 16 million miles from the earth afforded an opportunity for a new computation of the astronomical unit. The previous computation had been done by Mr. A. R. Hinks from the approach of Eros in 1900–1, and as a result of this the astronomical unit was given as 92,900,000 miles, but Sir Harold S. Jones's work makes it a little larger—93,005,000 miles. If we adopt this value the sun's parallax is very easily found by the method previously described, and is $3963 \cdot 5 \times 206265/93,005,000 = 8 \cdot 790$ seconds. Twenty-four observatories in different parts of the world co-operated in observing Eros—an indication of the amount of work involved.

When the sun's mean distance from the earth is known, the diameter of the sun is found by measuring his angular diameter. This varies according to the position of the earth in its orbit, being greatest when the earth is nearest the sun about January 4, and least when the earth is at its greatest distance from the sun on July 4. As the eccentricity of the earth's orbit is known with great accuracy its distance from the sun in miles on any date can be computed. The semi-diameter (not the diameter) of the sun is given in the Nautical Almanac for each day of the year and its value at the mean distance of the earth from the sun is accepted as $16' \ 01 \cdot 18''$ or $961 \cdot 18$ seconds. Hence the sun's radius is $961 \cdot 18 \times 93,005,000/206,265$ or about 433,000 miles.

Finding the Mass of the Sun

The mass of the sun can be computed in terms of the mass of the earth by making use of Kepler's third law. We have seen that the relation $T^2 = a^3$ holds for all bodies in the solar system, but there is no reason why the formula should not be applied to other systems as well. There is nothing unique about the sun that monopolizes this simple relation, and if we deal with another body, star or planet, the same law holds, provided we introduce a factor depending on the mass of the attracting body. If the sun had half his present mass the above relation would be expressed in the form $a^3 = \frac{1}{2}T^2$, if three times his present mass it would be $a^3 = 3T^2$, and so on. It is unnecessary to prove this relation at present and readers must be prepared to accept it. The subject is dealt with in Appendix VIII, to which those who desire fuller information can refer.

Now let us consider again the earth-moon system. On page 58 it has been shown how the mass of the moon is found in terms of the mass of the earth, and the combined mass of the system is $6 \cdot 05 \times 10^{27}$ gm. Apply the formula for Kepler's third law to the earth-moon system, remembering that T in this case is $0 \cdot 0748$ and that a is $0 \cdot 002571$, the value of T being the moon's sidereal period, expressed as a decimal of a year, and that of a being the moon's mean distance from the earth, expressed as a decimal of an astronomical unit. The formula connecting these can be written in the form

$$a^3 = kT^2, \text{ or } k = a^3/T^2$$

k being the ratio of the mass of the earth-moon system to the mass of the sun. Substituting the above values of T and a, we find

that $k = (0\cdot002571)^3/(0\cdot0748)^2 = 0\cdot000000016994415/0\cdot00559504$, or $0\cdot0000303741$. It is unnecessary to use all the figures in the cube of a and only six significant figures are taken. The mass of the earth-moon system is, therefore, $0\cdot0000303741$ that of the sun, or the sun is $329,228$ times the mass of the earth-moon system. Multiplying this last number by $6\cdot05 \times 10^{27}$, the mass of the sun is almost 2×10^{33} gm. or just under 2×10^{27} tons.

Weighing the Planets

This method can be used to weigh any of the planets which are attended by one or more satellites. Take, for instance, Mars which has two small satellites revolving round it. Phobos, the closer of the two to Mars, has a sidereal period of $0\cdot31801$ day, or $0\cdot0008731$ year, and its mean distance from Mars is $0\cdot000062725$ astronomical unit. Each of these can be expressed in the form, $T = 8\cdot731 \times 10^{-4}$, $a = 6\cdot2725 \times 10^{-5}$. Hence for Mars $k = 6\cdot272^3 \times 10^{-15}/ (8\cdot731 \times 10^{-4})^2$, using only four significant figures which are more than sufficient for the purpose. From the above we find $k = 3\cdot24 \times 10^{-7}$, and multiplying this by 2×10^{33} the mass of Mars is $6\cdot48 \times 10^{26}$ gms. The mass of the earth is $5\cdot98 \times 10^{27}$ gms., and hence the mass of Mars is about $0\cdot108$ that of the earth.

We can use Deimos, the other satellite of Mars, for the same purpose. In the case of this satellite $T = 3\cdot456 \times 10^{-3}$, $a = 1\cdot570 \times 10^{-4}$, hence $k = (1\cdot570 \times 10^{-4})^3 / (3\cdot456 \times 10^{-3})^2 = 3\cdot24 \times 10^{-7}$, the same figures as those obtained from the satellite Phobos.

This method has been used to find the masses of the planets which are attended by one or more satellites, and it supplies very accurate results. Strictly speaking, the figures obtained give the mass of the planet added to the total mass of its satellites, but as the latter is always very small in comparison with the mass of the planet itself, except in the case of the earth-moon system, no appreciable error occurs by considering that the results supply the mass of the planet itself. In the case of the planets which have no satellite, Mercury and Venus, and perhaps Pluto (but in the latter case a satellite, even if it existed, would be beyond the range of our telescopes), other methods for weighing them are adopted. The disturbance that a planet exercises on another planet, though small, is appreciable, and provides a method for estimating the mass of the disturbing body. Also, the disturbances that the planets exercise on comets supply the data for estimating their masses.

Finding the Diameters and Densities of the Planets

When the distance of a planet from the sun is known, its distance from the earth is easily found and then its diameter is computed from the angle which its disc subtends at the earth. Thus, on January 1, 1944, the polar diameter of Jupiter, which is then 429,764,000 miles from the earth, subtends an angle of 39·78 seconds at the earth. The polar diameter of Jupiter, is, therefore, $429,764,000 \times 39\cdot78/206,265 = 82,884$ miles. This method cannot be used for Pluto whose disc even as seen with the most powerful telescope is too small to give reliable results. For this reason the size of Pluto is very uncertain.

When the diameters and the masses of the planets are known, their densities are easily found. Dividing the mass of a planet, expressed in

grams, by its volume in cubic centimetres (the volume being derived from the diameter) gives its mean density, the density of water being the unit. The density of a planet at varying distances from the centre may differ considerably from the mean density. As we shall see later, in estimating the mean density of some of the larger planets, the diameters include their atmospheres, and obviously the density of the atmosphere is very small in comparison with that of any solid portion of the planet.

Finding the Orbital Velocities of the Planets

Kepler's second law is equivalent to saying that the nearer a planet is to the sun the greater is its speed, because in this case a longer arc is swept out by the planet to equalise the areas, hence it is easy to find the velocity of any planet in any portion of its orbit, provided its distance from the sun at the time is known, and also its mean distance from the sun.

Without going into a proof of the formula the following simple form for it can be accepted, a denoting the mean distance of the planet from the sun, and r its distance at the time when its orbital velocity, v in miles per second is required :

$$v = 18 \cdot 47 \sqrt{\frac{2}{r} - \frac{1}{a}}$$

Take the case of Mars whose mean distance from the sun is $1 \cdot 524$ astronomical units and whose greatest and least distances are $1 \cdot 675$ and $1 \cdot 390$, expressed in the same unit. In the first case $a = 1 \cdot 524$, $r = 1 \cdot 675$, and the value of the expression under the radical is $0 \cdot 733$. Hence $v = 18 \cdot 47 \times 0 \cdot 733 = 13 \cdot 5$ miles per second. In the second case where $r = 1 \cdot 390$ the value of the expression under the radical is $0 \cdot 885$. Hence $v = 18 \cdot 47 \times 0 \cdot 885 = 16 \cdot 3$ miles per second. The velocities of any of the planets can be found in the same way.

Bode's Law

Bode's Law is called after Johann Elert Bode, a German astronomer, born in 1747, though the name of Titius should be associated with that of Bode in discovering the law. Write down the numbers 0, 3, 6, 12, and so on, each number, except the first, being double the number preceding it. Add 4 to each of the numbers thus obtained and the result will give the *relative* mean distances of the planets from the sun, starting with Mercury, the planet nearest to the sun. The result of proceeding according to the above rule is shown below, and the actual mean distances of the planets are given for the sake of comparison.

Mercury	Venus	Earth	Mars	Asteroids	Jupiter	Saturn	Uranus	Neptune	Pluto
4	7	10	16	28	52	100	196	388	772

(By Bode's Law)

Mercury	Venus	Earth	Mars	Asteroids	Jupiter	Saturn	Uranus	Neptune	Pluto
3·9	7·2	10	15·2		52	95·4	192	300·7	390

(Actual Distances)

The *average* distance of the asteroids corresponds fairly well with the distance 28 supplied by the law. In other cases the law is approximately correct except in the cases of Neptune and Pluto. It is remarkable that Pluto is 39 astronomical units from the sun and that the law suggests nearly this distance for Neptune (actually 38·8).

If we deal with the distances of the planets from Mercury's orbit, then the law merely suggests distances increasing in geometrical progression with common ratio 2. In other words, the relative distances of the planets from the orbit of Mercury are as 3, 6, 12, 24, 48, etc.

This was pointed out by Mr. J. Miller in *Nature*, February 5, 1938 (**141**, 245), when he showed that this slight alteration in the usual form of stating the law led to some interesting results in Saturn's satellite system (applying the modified Bode's Law to the planets and their satellites). In a subsequent notice in *Nature*, October 8, 1938 (**142**, 670) Miller utilized his amended form to make certain predictions with regard to Jupiter's satellite system. At the time of writing, Dr. S. B. Nicholson had discovered two new satellites of Jupiter, and Miller predicted that one of them would be at a distance of 16 million miles from the planet and have retrograde motion. When its orbit was computed later the prediction was actually verified (its mean distance was found to be about 14 million miles and its motion was retrograde). His prediction about the other satellite, now named X, was not so fortunate, as he believed that it would lie in a vacant place between satellites IV and VI. In point of fact its mean distance from its primary was found to be almost the same as that of VI, but slightly greater. Satellites VI, VII and X lie nearly at the same mean distance from Jupiter and it is possible that they once formed a single body which was disrupted. Perhaps another satellite will some day be found in the 'vacant place' at a distance of about $3\frac{1}{2}$ million miles from Jupiter.

Bode's Law has been useful in searching for planets, as will be seen later. It is purely empirical, not being based on any dynamical principle, but it can scarcely be considered a coincidence.

Finding the Temperature of a Planet

The temperature of a planet can be found by using very sensitive instruments which will be described later, or it can be determined from theoretical considerations, and a description of this method follows. It will be seen later that the agreement between the different methods is very satisfactory.

We shall start with the earth and then show how a simple calculation enables us to find the temperature on any other planet. The effect of an atmosphere on a planet introduces certain complications, and we shall imagine that there are no atmospheres—a hypothesis which is true only for Mercury and the minor planets, and also for all the satellites.* In addition, in the first instance, it will be assumed that the planet always turns the same face to the sun, as Mercury does, the period of revolution being the same as its time of axial rotation. When the planet does not do so a correction can be applied which gives good results for the other planets that do not rotate on their axes in the same time in which they revolve round the sun.

We have already seen that 1·94 calories each minute fall on each square centimetre of the earth's surface, assuming that the radiation falls at right angles to the surface. When a condition of stability in receiving

*While reading these proofs, it was announced that Dr. Gerald P. Kuiper, at the McDonald Observatory, U.S.A., had discovered methane and possibly ammonia in the atmosphere of Titan, Saturn's largest satellite.

and radiating heat by the earth has been attained, the earth will remain at practically the same temperature which will be assumed to be T°.K. Stefan's Law states that the total energy of all wave lengths emitted per square centimetre by a 'black' body is proportional to the fourth power of its absolute temperature. If E is the energy the law can be expressed in the form,

$$E = kT^4, \text{ where } k \text{ is a constant.}$$

When the value of the constant, derived from experimental evidence, is introduced, the equation can be expressed in the form

$$E = 76 \cdot 8 \times 10^{-12} T^4 \text{ calories per minute.}$$

Assuming, then, that the earth radiates like a 'black' body and that it is radiating as much heat as it receives from the sun, we obtain the equation

$$76 \cdot 8 \times 10^{-12} T^4 = 1 \cdot 94 \text{ from which}$$
$$T^4 = 253 \times 10^8, \text{ or } T = 400° \text{ K. approximately.}$$

The radiation received from the sun varies inversely as the square of the distance of the body from the sun. From the diagram (Fig. 21) where S is a source of heat and AB, A'B' are two circular sections at distances

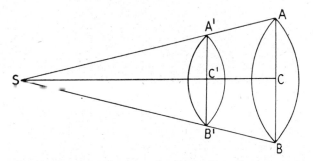

Fig. 21. The amount of heat falling on a surface varies inversely with the square of the distance of the surface from the source of heat. The diameters of the two circles AB and A'B' vary as their distances from the source, in accordance with the property of similar triangles, that is, SC/SC' = AB/A'B'. The areas of circles vary as the squares of their diameters, and hence they vary as the squares of the distances from the source. The same quantity of heat falls on each circle, and hence the amount on unit area varies inversely with the square of the distances of the surfaces from the source.

d and d' from S, the diameters of the sections are in the same ratio as their distances from S, and hence their areas are in the ratio of the squares of their distances from S. For this reason the amount of heat falling on a given area in the two sections is inversely as the squares of their distances from the source. If a planet is at a distance R astronomical units from the sun the radiation which it receives on unit area is $1/R^2$ that which the earth receives on the same area. The equation for finding T becomes, therefore,

$$76 \cdot 8 \times 10^{-12} T^4 = 1 \cdot 94/R^2, \text{ from which}$$
$$T = 400°/R^{\frac{1}{2}}.$$

Notice that this temperature applies only to the portion of the planet directly under the sun. On other portions the rays fall obliquely on the surface of the planet and the temperature in such parts is lower.

This last expression can be used to find the temperature of the side of Mercury which is continually exposed to the sun, assuming that it is nearest to the sun in its orbit, the distance being 0·306 of an astronomical unit. The square root of 0·306 is 0·553, and dividing this into 400 the result is 723°K. or 450° C.

When a planet rotates so that it does not expose the same face to the sun all the time, certain modifications are introduced. It is well known that the total radiation received on a hemisphere is the same as that received on a cross-sectional area equal to the area of a circle whose diameter is the same as that of the sphere. A proof of this is given in Appendix IX and readers must accept the statement for the present. Hence the total radiation received on a hemisphere of radius r is proportional to πr^2, but, as the planet is rotating, the total area of the planet, that is, $4\pi r^2$, is radiating heat away. (In the case where the planet turns the same face to the sun, only half the sphere is radiating heat, the side remote from the sun neither receiving nor radiating any heat.) Hence we derive the equation

$$76\cdot8 \times 10^{-12}T^4 \times 4\pi r^2 = 1\cdot94\pi r^2/R^2, \text{ from which}$$
$$T = 283°/R^{\frac{1}{4}}.$$

If R is 1, that is, if the planet is the earth, T = 283° K. or 10° C., which is not far from the mean temperature of the earth.

It should be noticed that the result is slightly modified by the presence of an atmosphere and also by the fact that the earth does not radiate like a 'black' body, and the same applies to most of the planets, but the results obtained in all cases are sufficiently accurate for practical purposes. Thus, if we take Jupiter whose mean distance from the sun is 5·2 astronomical units, the average temperature should be $283/\sqrt{5\cdot2} = 124°K.$ or $-149°$ C., and this agrees well with the temperature found by other methods.

The radiation received on the earth from the planets can be measured by different instruments. The thermo-couple consists of two short pieces of wire made of different materials, welded together end to end. The other ends are attached to wires that run to a very delicate galvanometer which can measure extremely minute currents of electricity. When the welded junction of the two metals is heated an electric current flows through the circuit and its amount depends on the amount of heating. The radiation from the planet is first collected by a telescope and the thermo-couple is placed in the focus of the object glass or mirror ; this ensures that as much of the radiation as possible is concentrated on the thermo-couple, thus intensifying the effect.

The bolometer is also used to find the radiation from a planet and its use depends on the principle that when a small strip of platinum is heated its resistance is increased and hence the strength of a current which is made to pass through the strip is decreased. The deflection of a galvanometer measures the strength of the current and hence the intensity of the radiation.

While the thermo-couple or the bolometer supplies the astronomer with the total radiation from a planet, neither of them takes any account of the absorption by the earth's atmosphere. A correction can be applied for this

and then the total planetary radiation is known. A difficulty arises at this point because some of the radiation is simply reflected sunlight which is useless for the purpose in view. The astronomer wants to know the amount of radiation from the planet itself, and fortunately it is easy to separate this from the reflected sunlight. The radiation from the reflected sunlight consists of waves which are of shorter wave-length than that from the planet itself, and so the former passes easily through a vessel of water which is opaque to the long-wave planetary portion. Hence it is easy to measure the true radiation from the planet. The total energy from all wave-lengths is proportional to the fourth power of the absolute temperature of the radiating body, in accordance with Stefan's law (see page 30), and for a fixed surface normal to the radiation is expressed in the form

$$E = 76 \cdot 8 \times 10^{-12} T^4 \text{ calories per minute, or}$$
$$T = \sqrt[4]{E/76 \cdot 8} \times 10^3 = 332 \sqrt[4]{E}$$

Knowing E, the value of T can be found. For a rotating planet $T = 235 \sqrt[4]{E}$. (See p. 77).

The long-wave infra-red radiation does not pass easily through planetary atmospheres. It is well known that relatively short wave radiation, passing through the atmosphere, is converted into radiation of longer wave-length which does not readily pass out again. For this reason the presence of an atmosphere causes the temperature of a planet to rise, the atmosphere exercising a blanketing effect. Also an atmosphere restricts the rate and amount of variation on any planet. The earth's atmosphere exercises a moderating influence on the day and night temperatures.

CHAPTER VI

THE PLANETS: SPECIAL DETAILS

Mercury

IN GREEK MYTHOLOGY MERCURY WAS THE HERALD AND SWIFT-FOOTED messenger of the gods, and he was the patron of herdsmen, travellers, and thieves. In addition to wearing a winged cap and winged sandals, he carried a golden wand as a sign of his office, and this 'caduceus,' as it was called, had two wings at the top and two golden snakes twined around it. Stories are told of his mischievous pranks when he was only just big enough to walk about, and he seems to have possessed a wonderful aptitude for covering up his tracks and concealing his movements so that he would not be found out. Perhaps the name given to the nearest planet to the sun is appropriate because the planet Mercury is very elusive and it is probably true to say that a great number of people have never seen it.

Visibility of Mercury

The fact that Mercury lies between the earth and the sun explains why it is impossible to see it late at night. Fig. 22 brings out this point more clearly. When the planet is at its greatest distance from the sun lines drawn from the earth to the sun and to Mercury cannot contain an angle greater than 28°, but when it is nearest to the sun this angle cannot exceed 18°. Hence it is useless trying to find Mercury at an angle from the

sun greater than 28°, and generally the angle is much smaller than this. Of course, the angle may be 0° when the sun, Mercury and the earth are in a line. The name *elongation* is given to this angle, and when the elongation is west, Mercury sets before and rises before the sun. In September and October the planet is most conspicuous at greatest western elongation and can be seen in the morning hours. At its greatest eastern elongation

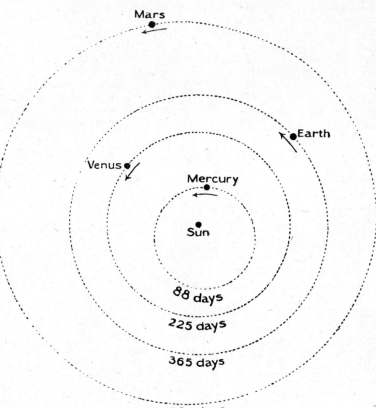

Fig. 22. The eccentric orbit of Mercury is shown, that of Mars being less eccentric, while the orbit of Venus is seen to be practically a circle. Whatever the position of the earth may be it is obvious that Mercury will never be far from the direction of the sun, and hence the planet can never be seen late at night long after sunset.

it can be best seen as an evening star in March and April. Although at these times it appears as a bright star, it is near the horizon when the sun is near the horizon, and cannot be seen for long after sunrise or sunset. Owing to its small size it twinkles like a star, unlike the other planets. Mercury is utterly devoid of an atmosphere.

Although Mercury cannot be seen with the naked eye during the hours of bright sunshine, the position of the planet is known to the astronomer at any hour on any day, and he can set his telescope to the exact spot where Mercury is. As might be expected, the planet shows phases just

like the moon, being a crescent when it is nearly between the earth and the sun, and showing the full disc when it is on the other side of the sun. In intermediate positions it appears to have quarters like the moon. (See Fig. 23.)

Under the best conditions it is difficult to see the markings on the surface, but photographs show that there are such things. In spite of the fact that the markings have been photographed, the rotation period remained in doubt for a long time, but it is now accepted that this corresponds with its period of revolution round the sun, that is, 88 days. Mercury is so small and so near the sun that the powerful tides caused by the sun slowed down its rate of rotation until it became the same as the time of revolution. These were not necessarily oceanic tides ; it is more likely that they were in the molten interior of the planet, or that they are in the molten interior still, because there is no proof that Mercury is a solid body like a rock. When the crust forms on a planet it traps the internal heat and hence the interior of the planet cools very slowly.

Rotation of the Major Axis of Mercury's Orbit

On the whole Mercury seems to be a very uninteresting planet, but while this may be true from the point of view of the observer, nevertheless from the point of view of the dynamical astronomer it is probably the most interesting planet in the solar system. The major axis of the orbit of Mercury is slowly rotating owing to the disturbances produced by Venus and other planets. This rotation is at the rate of 574 seconds of arc per century. The dynamical astronomer can compute what the rate of rotation should be, taking into consideration the perturbations of the planets, and the figures for this are only 534 seconds per century.

The most likely assumption is that another planet exists between Mercury and the sun, and that this planet is so small that it has escaped detection. Indeed, Le Verrier computed the distance of this planet from the sun and gave it the name 'Vulcan,' but this hypothetical planet was never seen, in spite of the most careful search, including those carried out during total eclipses when it would be easier to find it. It is now generally believed that such a planet does not exist. Another theory, advocated by Seeliger, was that very diffuse matter in the neighbourhood of the orbit of Mercury is retarding its motion, but this theory has been shown to be untenable.

It almost seems that Mercury the planet is as impish as the Mercury of Greek mythology, and that the main purpose of its existence is to discredit the work of the dynamical astronomers. Now, however, we know that the planet is not so impish as it appeared for a long time, and indeed it has rendered invaluable assistance in the progress of science. The discrepancy of about 40 seconds has been laid by the heels since Einstein's general theory of relativity was successful in predicting an advance of 43 seconds a century above that predicted by the Newtonian theory of gravitation. Einstein's theory is too abstruse for this work, and it will be sufficient at this stage to say that the Newtonian laws are not absolutely rigorous, though for most of the astronomer's work it is impossible to detect any variation from absolute accuracy. In some cases, however, including the rotation of the axis major of Mercury's orbit, and the bending of light in the neighbourhood of the sun, the Newtonian laws are not

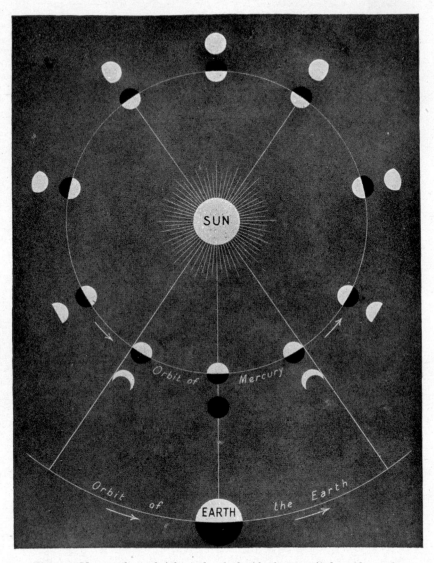

Fig. 23. Mercury has a bright and a dark side, because it depends on the sun for its illumination. From the earth we see different proportions of the illuminated hemisphere, and when the planet lies between the earth and the sun we see no illumination. The state of affairs as seen by an observer on a line through the Sun perpendicular to the ecliptic is shown by the inner circle, and the outer circle shows the appearances from the earth.

F

sufficiently accurate and Einstein's theory provides the necessary accuracy, producing accordance between theory and observation. To Mercury is due the credit for providing the first physical test between theory and observation, and going a long way towards justifying Einstein's theory.

Venus

Venus, the goddess of love and beauty, was born from the foam of the sea. Her chariot was drawn by doves and surrounded by flocks of little birds. It is related how she followed the young and beautiful Adonis when he went out hunting, as she was afraid some accident might befall him. Jupiter gave her to Vulcan in gratitude for the services that he had rendered in forging thunderbolts. Vulcan was the god of fire who presided over the working of metals, and the most beautiful of goddesses thus became the wife of the most ill-favoured of gods.

Phases of Venus

The planet Venus is the brightest of all the planets and indeed is brighter than any of the heavenly bodies except the sun and moon. Her orbit lies between those of Mercury and the earth, and the planet makes a close approach to the earth at times, coming within 26 million miles from us. Because her orbit is within that of the earth she shows phases just as Mercury does, and her appearance as a crescent or at the quarters as seen

FIG. 24. THE PHASES OF VENUS

When she is nearly in a line between the earth and the sun she appears as a crescent, shown on the right. As she recedes from the direction of the sun, as seen from the earth, she undergoes phases just like the moon and Mercury.

through a telescope is very beautiful. (See Fig. 24.) When Venus is east of the sun she sets after the sun and is seen as an evening star, and when west of the sun she sets and rises before the sun, appearing as a morning star.

The best telescopes fail to show any well-defined markings on the disc of Venus, and for this reason there have been conflicting views regarding her period of rotation. The evidence of the spectroscope in comparatively recent times shows that Venus rotates much more slowly than the earth does, though her periods of rotation and revolution are

not the same, as they are in the case of Mercury. At present it is believed that the rotation period is about 30 days, but this may be in error by several days.

The Atmosphere of Venus

The atmosphere of Venus contains carbon dioxide in abundance, but neither water-vapour nor oxygen has been detected. The layer of thick cloud which prevents us from seeing the actual surface of the planet prevents us also from detecting the constitution of the atmosphere bel ow this cloud. Slipher and Adel at the Lowell Observatory estimated that the air of Venus above the cloud contains a quantity of carbon dioxide equal to a layer two miles thick on the earth's surface. The atmosphere at low elevations may be very different from what it is above the cloud layer, and this fact makes it difficult to say whether life exists on the planet. If the carbon dioxide is plentiful in the atmosphere of Venus far below the cloud and there is vegetation, this vegetation would liberate free oxygen from the carbon dioxide that it absorbs. If there is free oxygen there may also be animal life, but we can only speculate on the form that it would take. It is reasonable to suppose that if there is no vegetable life, and therefore no free oxygen, there is no animal life.

The cloud layer is responsible for reflecting 59 per cent of the light of the sun that falls on Venus, and hence her bright appearance. Only 7 per cent of the light falling on Mercury or the moon is reflected—a remarkable contrast with Venus. The name *albedo* is given to the ratio between the total amount of radiation reflected by a body to the amount that falls on its surface. From the albedo it is possible to derive some information regarding the composition of the surface of a body. Thus, in the case of the moon, the albedo is consistent with her surface being composed of greyish-brown rocks. Measurements made of the reflection of light from a distant cliff on the earth show that its albedo is similar to that of Mercury and the moon. The albedo of Venus is what we should expect from a canopy of clouds which are capable of reflecting more light than is generally believed.

Transits of Venus

We have already shown how Eros has been used to find the distance of the sun from the earth. Before Eros was used for this purpose the transits of Venus across the sun's-disc afforded the means for determining the value of the astronomical unit, but the results lacked the precision of modern methods. A brief outline of the method used during the transit of Venus follows.

Imagine two observatories separated as far as possible on the surface of the earth, and astronomers in each watching the transit of Venus. Obviously, they will see the planet moving across the sun's disc in apparently different paths, see Fig. 25. The lengths of the tracks can be found from the *times* that the planet requires in each case to pass from limb to limb of the sun. Knowing the lengths, the places of the tracks on the sun's disc can be found and hence the displacement due to the different positions of the observatories. The amount of this displacement provides the necessary data for finding the distance of Venus from the earth, and, as shown on page 71, the scale of the solar system—the length of an astronomical unit—is calculated.

Neither Mercury nor Venus is attended by a satellite and they are the only planets, with the possible exception of Pluto, which have not one or more satellites revolving around them. The fact that there is no satellite attending either of these planets makes it more difficult to determine their masses, but, as pointed out on page 73, there are other ways for computing the masses of planets besides that based on the distances and

Fig. 25. A transit of Venus takes place when the planet passes across the sun's disc, between the sun and the earth. If a transit is observed at the same time from two places on the earth, the planet will appear to follow different paths across the sun's disc. Knowing the distance between the two places on the earth, which should be as far apart as possible, and knowing also the angular distance between the two paths, we can find the distance of the sun from the earth.

times of revolutions of their satellites. Venus has sometimes been called the earth's twin sister because her size, density and mass are not very far from those of the earth. Here, however, the similarity ends, and it is certain that the physical conditions on the surface of Venus have very little resemblance to those on our planet.

Mars

In Greek mythology Mars was the god of war, and he loved fighting and bloodshed for its own sake. His dislike of everything gentle and

beautiful is shown by his intense hatred of the beautiful Adonis. One day he sent an ugly wild boar to attack the boy with his sharp tusks, and a few hours later Venus found Adonis dying as a result of his wounds. Her tears turned to wind-flowers as they touched the ground and every drop of blood that fell from Adonis became a red rose. It is not surprising that Hippolyte, the queen of the Amazons, a race of warrior women who lived on the Caucasus Mountains and on the borders of the Black Sea, should have been presented by Mars with a famous girdle whose magic power made the charge of the Amazons like an irresistible storm.

Mars is the first planet outside the earth and can always be recognized by its ruddy colour. In certain respects it is the most interesting of all the planets because the conditions on it are not opposed to the existence of life, vegetable and animal. This does not necessarily imply that life in any form actually exists on Mars, but it may be presumed that when conditions are favourable, life will appear. At present there is much doubt as to what life really is and we can only conjecture how it originated on the earth. It probably has existed on our planet for a thousand million years and during this period it has assumed many strange forms, a great number of which have become extinct. There is no *a priori* reason why life should not have started on Mars thousands of millions of years ago, nor is there any reason why it should or should not have developed into forms very much higher than those on the earth—even including man himself.

Physical Features of Mars

The appearance of Mars when viewed through a telescope is utterly different from that of Venus. We saw that the surface of Venus was never visible, but the surface of Mars presents many interesting features when examined with the aid of the telescope. The first view of the planet, even through a large telescope, is certain to be disappointing, especially if the one who views it has seen some of the details of drawings of Mars. Amateurs are apt to forget that such details are given by trained observers who have spent many years studying the Martian features, and probably when they had their first view they saw little more than the amateur does when he looks at Mars for the first time. After some practice certain details are easily seen and these have a considerable amount of interest for astronomers.

The white polar caps are conspicuous at each pole during the winter on each hemisphere, and their shrinkage during the approach of summer can be followed. The southern cap is larger than the northern one, and it might be expected that the caps are snow, like the polar caps on the earth, but there is some doubt about this, and this doubt has been substantiated through the results of photographs of Mars with colour filters. When the sun is near the horizon the reddening effect shows that red light has the power to penetrate farther through the atmosphere than the blue or violet light. This is a well-known fact, and the longer the wave-length the greater the power of penetration through an atmosphere. Assuming that Mars has an atmosphere, an assumption which is correct, though it is very rarefied in comparison with the atmosphere of the earth, it is obvious that the best view of the surface of the planet should be obtained by exposing plates behind red filters. If violet filters are used we should expect that the atmospheric features would be emphasized in the photo-

graphs. W. H. Wright at the Lick Observatory found that the polar caps appeared very faint, or sometimes not at all, when red filters were used, but with the ultra-violet filters they were quite prominent. These results suggest that the polar caps are not surface markings but are atmospheric phenomena. It has been suggested, however, that below the atmospheric 'cap' there is a smaller surface cap.

The 'Canals' of Mars

The 'canals' of Mars were discovered by Schiaparelli in 1877, and as a result of a misunderstanding some confusion resulted from which many people are still suffering the effects. Schiaparelli saw narrow streaks which connected up larger dark markings, and he gave the name 'canali' to these streaks. The Italian word 'canale,' plural 'canali,' means a channel, or a canal, and the latter word was adopted amongst English-speaking people who always associate the word 'canal' with an artificial construction. The view that vast irrigation works had been undertaken by the inhabitants of Mars to convey water from polar to arid equatorial regions, quickly laid hold of people's imagination. Professor Lowell, in particular, was very much impressed with the idea and spent most of his life in studying the Martian 'canals.' An English engineer worked out the details of the scheme, showing the horse power of the pumps, the manner of utilizing the water, the number of square miles under cultivation on Mars, and requiring irrigation, etc. It is not surprising that public interest should have been aroused by considerations of intelligent life on another planet, but the scientist is less liable to be carried away by sentiment than the general public, and, to do justice to the British astronomers, they always received the theory of artificial 'canals' with a certain amount of reserve and often with intense suspicion. It is not denied that the so-called canals exist ; what is denied is that they have the uniform and geometrical characteristics of the canals as Lowell depicted them.

The late E. W. Maunder, when he was on the staff of the Royal Observatory, Greenwich, carried out a number of experiments with about two hundred boys of Greenwich Hospital School, with the assistance of the headmaster. A diagram was made, based upon drawings of Mars made by Schiaparelli, Lowell or other Martian observers, but the canals were not inserted. Instead of the canals a few dots and irregular markings were put in here and there. The boys were placed at various distances from the diagram and told to draw just what they saw. The irregular markings were detected and were properly represented by those nearest to the diagram, but those at the greatest distance were unable to see these markings, and reproduced the main features only—continents and seas. The most interesting results were obtained by the drawings of the boys in the intermediate position. They were not able to define the minute markings, though they were sufficiently close for the markings to produce some effect on them. *The impression was of a network of straight lines, occasionally with dots at the points of meeting of the lines.* (See Fig. 26.)

At a certain distance the chief canals drawn by Schiaparelli and Lowell had been 'seen' by the boys, in other words, they had interpreted the dots and irregular markings inserted by Mr. Maunder as the 'canals.' It may be worth remarking that none of the boys knew anything about

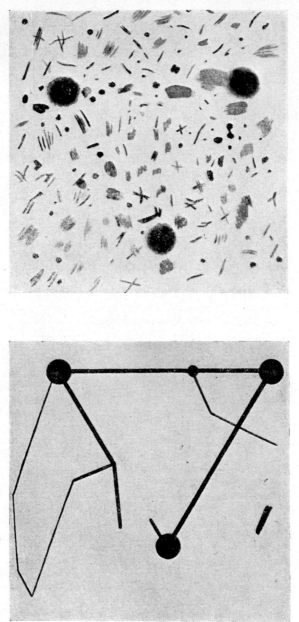

Fig. 26. The top diagram shows a number of irregular patches, and the lower diagram shows how the eye construes them when they are placed at a distance of 30 feet. The diagrams illustrate the difficulty of interpreting correctly the markings on the surface of Mars, which some astronomers thought were canals constructed by the inhabitants to irrigate the arid regions.

Mars before the experiment, and hence there was no possibility of bias. Mr. Maunder had made similar experiments about twelve years before this, and these experiments, privately conducted, led him to the conclusion, published in 1894, that the canals of Mars were simply the summation of a complexity of detail too minute to be separately discerned.

Readers can try an experiment for themselves which will corroborate Mr. Maunder's conclusions. On a piece of cardboard draw a number of dots—about five to the inch—nearly in a line, and make each dot large enough to be seen about thirty feet away. Invite someone who knows nothing about the experiment to stand about thirty feet from the cardboard and to tell you what he sees. It is almost certain that he will say he sees a *line*, but if you show him the dots first of all, he will most probably interpret them as dots. For the same reason, markings on Mars which appear to be continuous, are not necessarily continuous, and even the most experienced observer can be misled by the telescopic appearance of the surface of the planet.

The Martian Atmosphere

The atmosphere of Mars is very much rarer than that of the earth, and spectroscopic analysis of the oxygen content shows that this is very small. Not only is oxygen scarce ; the amount of water vapour is only about 5 per cent that above an equal area on the earth's surface. It has been suggested that the general ruddy colour of Mars is due to the oxydized rocks which have abstracted the greater part of the oxygen from the Martian atmosphere. If the rocks have been responsible for taking the oxygen from the atmosphere, this would explain the small amount of oxygen detected in the Martian atmosphere but, owing to the low velocity of escape (see page 50), it is possible to explain the low oxygen content by assuming that the molecules have gone off into space in the course of hundreds of millions of years (see page 60). It is difficult to say how far the present amount of oxygen is capable of supporting animal life. Under terrestrial conditions life, as we know it, would not be able to exist, but we know that life is very adaptable, and it is possible that a very rarefied atmosphere could support animal life which had developed to suit its environment.

The seasonal changes in the dark markings on Mars have been attributed to vegetable life, growth and subsidence producing the effects well-known to astronomers. The presence of vegetation demands the presence of carbon dioxide also, and although the latter has not been detected, this is no proof that it is non-existent. Carbon dioxide must be present in a fairly large amount before it can be detected, and it is quite possible that this gas and also vegetation exist. If we accept the presence of vegetable life on Mars it seems very difficult to deny the presence of animal life as well, because the line of demarcation between the vegetable and the animal in its lowest stage is not always easy to define. Even if animal life does exist on the planet there is no proof that it has evolved into the higher forms that we find on the earth. Neither is there any proof that it has not so evolved, and we can only speculate on the subject.

The Satellites of Mars

Mars has two very small satellites or moons which have been named Phobos and Deimos. Phobos has a diameter of about 10 miles, but the actual figure is very doubtful as the disc of the satellite is too small for accurate measurement. Its mean distance from Mars is 5,828 miles, and it revolves round the planet in 7 hours 39 minutes. This is about one-third of the period of rotation of Mars, and hence the satellite, as seen from Mars, rises in the west and sets in the east in a Martian day. Deimos, the outer satellite, has a diameter about half that of Phobos, and revolves around Mars in 30 hours at a mean distance of 14,600 miles. Like Phobos, it revolves in the same direction in which Mars rotates—a common feature of the satellites but there are notable exceptions to which we shall refer later.

It has been pointed out that these satellites are very useful to the astronomer in providing the data for weighing Mars. Those who are conversant with Dean Swift's *Gulliver's Travels* will remember that there is reference to the astronomers on the island of Laputa whose telescopes discovered two moons revolving round Mars, one completing a revolution in ten hours and the other in twenty-one and a half hours. It is remarkable that Dean Swift should have made such a prediction—not very far from the truth—about a century and a half before the moons were discovered.

Jupiter

Jupiter was the king and father of gods and men and lived above the clouds on Mount Olympus with the other gods. He was the strongest of all the gods and used thunderbolts as his weapon. It is told that after the Golden Age when men became quarrelsome and wicked Jupiter decided that he would destroy them. Shutting up the North Wind in the cave of Aeolus he sent forth the South Wind that brought torrents of rain, and all the human family, except Deucalion and Pyrrha, who had not become wicked like the others, was destroyed by the Great Deluge.

It is very fitting that the giant planet of the solar system should be named Jupiter. Its mass is greater than that of all the other planets combined, and it has more satellites than any of the other planets. Even a small telescope shows the equatorial bulge and the polar flattening of Jupiter, due to his rapid speed of rotation in 9 hours 55 minutes. Compared with the earth's rate of rotation this may not seem very rapid, but as the equatorial diameter of Jupiter is more than eleven times that of the earth the speed of rotation at Jupiter's equator is about twenty-seven times as great as that at the equator of the earth. So great is Jupiter's equatorial bulge that the difference between his equatorial and polar diameters is nearly 6,000 miles. The difference between the value of gravity at Jupiter's equator and poles is much greater than in the case of the earth ; the same also applies to the planet Saturn.

Surface Features of Jupiter

The surface features of Jupiter are interesting and a small telescope shows the *belts*—dark streaks parallel to the equator of the planet. A large telescope reveals that the belts are undergoing rapid changes of

form—an indication that they are not on the solid surface of Jupiter but are in the atmosphere. The *north and south equatorial belts*, which are about 10° on either side of the equator, are the most conspicuous of the belts, and they include within their boundaries the bright *equatorial zone*. The *north and south tropical zones* lie in higher latitudes than the equatorial belts, and less conspicuous belts lie beyond these until we come to the polar regions of Jupiter. Markings on Jupiter are less obvious than those on Mars but they are sufficiently well defined to determine the period of rotation very accurately. We have seen that the sun's period of rotation varies with the latitude, and the same is true of Jupiter. The mean period of the equatorial zone is 9 hours 50 minutes 26 seconds and in other parts of the disc it varies from 9 hours 55 minutes 5 seconds to about 37 seconds longer than this last period. The different rates of rotation suggest that we are not looking on a solid body as in the case of Mars but that we see the atmosphere of Jupiter only. It is now believed that the atmosphere is very thick—some estimates place it at 6,000 miles— and that a layer of ice exists underneath it. The low mean density of the planet, 1·34, shows that there must be a considerable portion of the apparent disc which is not in the solid condition, unlike Mercury and Mars, in which the solid surfaces are easily seen.

The spectroscope has shown that the Jovian atmosphere consists mainly of ammonia and methane. The latter has the chemical formula CH_4 and is commonly known as marsh-gas and also as firedamp. It is found in large quantities in coal mines, because it is one of the products of the decomposition which has resulted in the formation of the coal-measures. It is also found in marshy places—hence one of its names— owing to the decomposition of vegetable matter, and can be released from the bottom of ponds by gently disturbing the mud at the bottom. Jupiter and the other major planets, Saturn, Uranus and Neptune, all possess methane as a constituent of their atmospheres, but Saturn has relatively more of this gas than Jupiter has. It has been shown that these two gases are what we should expect on massive planets with low temperatures. It may be noticed that hydrogen forms a large part of the atmosphere but not free hydrogen. It is associated with carbon, forming methane, or with nitrogen, forming ammonia, NH_3, and hence the hydrogen could not have escaped from the major planets as it has done from Mars and largely from the earth. This is easily explained when it is remembered that the velocity of escape on the major planets is much higher than it is on the earth, and hence hydrogen would not be so likely to fly off into space. By following the course of events on the major planets from the time when they were very hot until the time when they were cold bodies, and by considering the various chemical reactions that would occur, it appears that ammonia and methane are the chief gases that we should expect to find on them. In the case of two of the major planets, Uranus and Neptune, the ammonia is frozen owing to the low temperature. It may be assumed that life on any of the major planets is very improbable unless it exists in some form of which we have no conception with our limited outlook.

The Satellites of Jupiter

Four of Jupiter's eleven satellites can be easily seen with binoculars and were discovered by Galileo in 1610 with his home-made telescope.

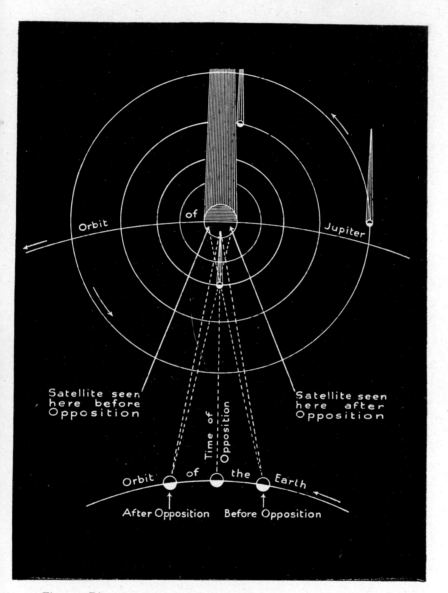

Fig. 27. Diagramatic representation of the eclipses and transits of Jupiter's four larger satellites. When the satellites pass in front of Jupiter they cast shadows on the bright surface of the planet, and these can be seen as little round spots. On the other side of Jupiter the satellites pass into the shadow of the planet, which intercepts part of the light from the sun, and are eclipsed. In addition to this, they may be hidden from our view by Jupiter himself, though not in his shadow, and are then said to be occulted.

They revolve round Jupiter in nearly circular orbits and the planes of their orbits lie close to the plane of the planet's equator. As Jupiter's polar axis is nearly perpendicular to the plane of the ecliptic, the four satellites move close to the plane of the ecliptic. As with the moon, so with Jupiter's satellites, each rotates in the same period as it takes to revolve round the planet, another instance of the effect of tidal friction. The other seven satellites are fainter and more difficult to see, and three of them have retrograde motion, that is, they revolve round Jupiter in a direction opposite to that of the planet's rotation and of its revolution round the sun.

As Jupiter's four brightest satellites revolve round their primary they pass behind the planet and through his shadow, or between the earth and the planet when their shadows are cast on Jupiter. A full explanation of the phenomena of the satellites is given in Fig. 27, and it is very interesting to watch these with the aid of a small telescope. The times of the occurrences of the various phenomena are given in the *Nautical Almanac* and those who are interested in observing the satellites should consult this publication so that they can know beforehand what to look for.

Jupiter's Satellites and the Velocity of Light

As long ago as 1675 the Danish astronomer Roemer noticed that there were discrepancies in the observed times of eclipses of Jupiter's satellites. When the earth was near Jupiter the eclipses occurred earlier than they did when the earth was at a greater distance from Jupiter, or earlier than the average, and when the earth was far off from Jupiter they were later than the average and later still in comparison with the time when the earth was near Jupiter. Roemer was not the first to make this discovery but he was the first to explain the reason for the phenomenon. He pointed out that light did not travel with an infinite velocity and hence required a longer time to reach the earth when an eclipse of Jupiter's satellite occurred while the earth was in a part of its orbit far off from Jupiter than when it was in a part nearer to Jupiter. This discovery afforded one method of measuring the velocity of light. Several other methods, involving only terrestrial apparatus, have been used, and greater accuracy has been attained with various refinements and improvements. The most recent determination of the velocity of light *in vacuo* is 186,271 miles or 299,774 kilometres a second. For ordinary purposes the velocity of light is frequently taken as 3×10^{10} cm./sec.

Saturn

Saturn was an old Italian deity and it is told that when he was dethroned by Jupiter he fled to Italy where he reigned during the Golden Age. The feast of Saturnalia was held every year in memory of his beneficent reign, and during this time, corresponding to the winter solstice, public business was suspended, slaves were indulged with great liberties, great feasts took place, and friends made presents to one another. It is probably well known to the reader that the Roman Saturnalia was taken over by the Christian Church in the fifth century and recognized as the time of the birth of Christ, though there is no historical evidence that Christ was born at this time of the year. December was the

height of the rainy season in Judea when neither shepherds nor flocks would have been in the fields of Bethlehem at night. It may have been due to tradition that December 25th was finally adopted as the day of Christ's birth, but it is much more probable that it was the desire to supplant heathen festivals.

Features of Saturn

Saturn is the next planet as we travel out from the sun and ranks next to Jupiter in size. Its rotation period is 10 hours 14 minutes and the difference between its equatorial and polar diameters is 7,900 miles— more than in the case of Jupiter in spite of the fact that the planet is smaller than Jupiter. The oblateness of a planet depends on the ratio of the centrifugal force to the acceleration of gravity at the equator, and also on the distribution of the material in the planet's interior. The mass of Jupiter is highly concentrated towards its centre and this accentuates the oblateness due to ratio of the centrifugal force to the acceleration of gravity, but the concentration must be greater still in the case of Saturn. It is surprising to learn that the mean density of the planet is only 0·69, so that it would float if we could imagine it immersed in an enormous ocean of water. This statement may be a little misleading because we spoke of the *mean density*, but it is obvious that a very thick atmosphere exists around Saturn and this is included in its diameter. As explained previously (see page 73), when the distance of a planet is known its diameter is easily found from the angle subtended by the diameter at the earth. The astronomer has no choice but to include the atmosphere of Saturn in the angular diameter, just as with Jupiter. For this reason, when the density is computed from the mass and diameter, the fictitious diameter, which includes the atmosphere, will be responsible for giving a lower density than would occur if the diameter of the solid portion only were taken into consideration. The atmosphere of Saturn consists of ammonia and methane but the amount of ammonia is less than is found in the atmosphere of Jupiter. This is easily explained by the fact that ammonia freezes at a higher temperature than methane, and therefore on Saturn, the temperature of which is lower than on Jupiter, relatively less ammonia would be present in the atmosphere. The clouds on Saturn are arranged in bands but not in such a regular manner as on Jupiter, and they are less distinct than those on Jupiter, as we might expect from the greater distance of Saturn. It is believed that a thick layer of ice lies underneath the atmosphere and a rocky core under the ice, but we can only conjecture regarding the physical conditions on the planet, because it is impossible to penetrate through the envelope of clouds, and underneath these the planet is wrapped in mystery.

Saturn's System of Rings

The ring system of Saturn is one of the most beautiful sights in the heavens when seen through a moderate-sized telescope, but even a small telescope will show the rings if they are well placed for observation. (See Fig. 28.) The system is divided into the crape or dusky ring which starts about 7,000 miles from the equator of Saturn and extends for 11,500 miles. Then a gap of 1,000 miles occurs before we reach the inner

bright ring which is 16,000 miles across. Another gap, known as Cassini's Division, 3,000 miles wide, then occurs before we reach the outer bright ring. The far edge of the outer bright ring is about 86,000 miles from the centre of the planet, and if we measure across from the inner edge of the crape ring to the outer edge of the outer ring the distance is 41,000 miles. The rings are relatively thin—probably much less than 50 miles and perhaps not much more than 10 miles. It is obviously impossible to measure such a small thickness with precision at a distance of about 800 million miles.

The name ring may be misleading because it conveys the idea of a

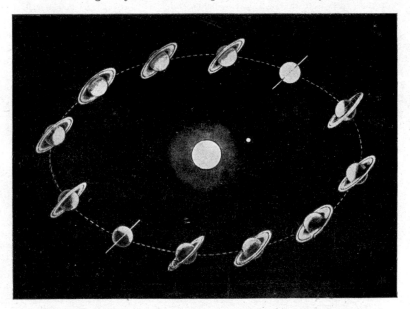

Fig. 28. The phases of Saturn's rings. The axis of Saturn, like that of the earth, is inclined to the plane of the ecliptic and for half the planet's year of 29½ of our years, the sun shines on its north pole and on the northern face of the ring. If the north pole of the planet is tilted towards the earth at this time the rings are easily seen. The diagram shows the plane of the ring passing through the sun in two positions, and as the ring is very thin, it vanishes at such times. The earth is represented by the small bright spot nearly right of the sun.

solid structure and indeed when the rings are seen through a telescope they look like something solid belonging to the planet. The brilliant mathematical analysis of James Clerk Maxwell showed that the rings could not be solid, but consisted of myriads of small bodies, each moving in its own orbit round the planet. The bodies must be very small, many of them being merely like grains of sand, though many are much larger than this, and they reflect the light of the sun falling on them, so that we see them just as we see the moon or the satellites of other planets. The spectroscope shows that the inner portion of the ring is moving with a greater speed than the outer portion, thus supporting Maxwell's conclusions, because if they consisted of a solid ring, all parts would rotate in

the same period, and the outer portion, having a greater distance to move than the inner portion, in the same time, would have a greater velocity.

When we look at Saturn's rings we are almost certainly looking at the results of a celestial catastrophe. The heavenly bodies do not exercise undue disturbances on one another so long as they keep well apart. At the most they just pull one another out of their ordinary courses, altering the shapes of their orbits to an extent which depends upon their masses and their distances of approach. But if they come within a certain limit they will tear each other to pieces, or rather the heavier body will tear the smaller one into fragments. The name 'Roche Limit,' after Roche who formulated the law, is given to the least distance between the centres of two bodies before disruption due to attraction occurs.

Imagine one massive body, say Saturn, and a smaller body, say a satellite of Saturn, and also imagine that they have the same density. Now suppose that the satellite, which can be assumed to be a loose agglomeration of matter with little or no coherence, but held together by its own gravitation, approaches Saturn until the distance between their centres is $2 \cdot 44 \ r$, where r is the radius of Saturn. The satellite in these circumstances will be just within the Roche Limit and it will be disrupted by the planet. If the density of the satellite is $1/\rho$ that of the planet the distance of the Roche Limit will be $2 \cdot 44 \sqrt[3]{\rho}$. Suppose, for example, that the satellite has a density twice that of Saturn, so that $1/\rho$ is 2, or ρ is $\frac{1}{2}$, the satellite could then venture within $2 \cdot 44 \sqrt[3]{\frac{1}{2}} = 1 \cdot 94$ radii of Saturn before it would be disrupted. If the density of the satellite were $\frac{1}{2}$ that of Saturn, ρ is 2, and the distance for safety would be $2 \cdot 44 \sqrt[3]{2} = 3 \cdot 07$ radii of Saturn. If the satellite were in the form of a solid rock, in which case cohesion would be considerable, the above results would require modification, but we need not consider this particular case.

It is fairly certain that in the remote past a satellite had ventured too close to Saturn and was disrupted. It is not so certain what was the cause of its meandering into danger, but perhaps it was once an outsider—a small body which was not part of Saturn's system—and during its motion through space it happened to come within Saturn's attractive force. The planet then drew it in closer and finally disrupted it. It may be pointed out that there is no satellite in the solar system which lies within the Roche Limit, though Phobos is not far outside it, and also that every part of Saturn's ring system is within the Roche Limit. Saturn's nearest satellite, Mimas, is at a distance of 115 thousand miles from the centre of the planet, and as Saturn's equatorial radius is 37,500 miles, the Roche Limit is at a distance $2 \cdot 44 \times 37,500 = 91,500$ miles. It is obvious that Mimas lies well outside the Roche Limit unless its density is considerably less than that of Saturn, which is very improbable. A simple calculation shows that if the density of Mimas were $0 \cdot 35$, that is, half the density of Saturn, it would be just within the Roche Limit and would be liable to disintegration. As it shows no signs of disintegration we may assume that its density is not as low as $0 \cdot 35$.

The Satellites of Saturn

Saturn has nine satellites, the largest of which is Titan. Its diameter is smaller than that of Mercury and it revolves round Saturn in 16 days. All Saturn's satellites, with the exception of Phoebe, the outermost one,

revolve in direct orbits. Satellites of Jupiter and Saturn very far from their primaries show this tendency to retrograde motion more than those that lie closer to the planet, and this phenomenon raises many problems in dynamical astronomy. No really satisfactory explanation has yet been given why these outer satellites should show this tendency, and probably no satisfactory explanation will be given until we know how the solar system originated. Although many theories have been advanced to explain how the planetary and satellite systems originated, serious objections have been brought forward against all of them, and the real origin of the planets and satellites still remains a mystery.

Uranus

In Greek mythology Uranus (heaven) is the husband of Gæa (earth) and father of Saturn and other deities. The planet Uranus was not known to the ancient astronomers though it is just within the range of visibility with the naked eye. Its discovery was accidental. In 1781 Sir William Herschel was observing with his reflecting telescope which he had made himself and saw an object in the constellation of Gemini. It seemed larger

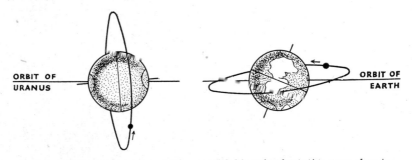

ORBIT OF URANUS

ORBIT OF EARTH

Fig. 29. Uranus moves round the sun with his axis of rotation very close to the plane of his orbit. The four satellites of Uranus move in orbits whose planes are nearly in the plane of the planet's equator. The circle and arrow show the orbit and direction of motion of one satellite, and these are typical of the others. The diagram also shows why the orbits of the satellites are presented to the earth at different angles, depending on the relative positions of the earth and Uranus. In the diagram the orbits are nearly flat side towards the earth, and in this position they appear nearly circular. In 1945 they will present an appearance similar to this. In 1924 they were edgewise to us.

than a star, and Herschel believed that the object was a comet. He kept it under observation for several weeks and from its positions the mathematical astronomers were able to compute its orbit and to pronounce that it was a planet. The planet had been observed many times by other astronomers before Herschel saw it, but they had not suspected that it was a planet. Herschel named the new planet Georgium Sidus in honour of King George III who knighted Herschel and appointed him his private astronomer. Other European astronomers called the planet Herschel, but, finally, on the suggestion of Bode, Director of the Berlin Observatory, it was called Uranus.

The Atmosphere of Uranus

Owing to the great distance of Uranus from the earth little detail can be seen of its surface markings, and its time of rotation cannot be determined by noticing its physical features through the telescope, as is done with Jupiter and Saturn. The spectroscope comes to the aid of the astronomer in this case, just as it is used to find the period of revolution of different parts of Saturn's rings, and it is found that Uranus rotates in a period of less than 11 hours.

Owing to the low temperature prevailing on Uranus the ammonia is frozen out of the atmosphere and methane is its chief constituent.

The Satellites of Uranus

The plane of the equator of Uranus is nearly at right angles to the plane of the ecliptic, and as the four satellites of the planet revolve close to the plane of the planet's equator, their orbits are nearly perpendicular to the plane of the ecliptic. (See Fig. 29.) To be exact, the orbits of the satellites are inclined at nearly 98° to the plane of the ecliptic so that their revolutions are retrograde. When the inclination of the plane of an orbit is greater than 90° the body has retrograde motion, and if it is exactly 90° the motion is neither direct nor retrograde. Fig. 29 also shows why the orbits of the satellites are presented to observers on the earth at different angles. In 1924 they were edgewise to us and in 1945 they will appear nearly circular.

Neptune

Neptune, a brother of Jupiter, ruled the sea. It is told that when the gods fought against the unruly Titans—a race of giants—and conquered them, the Titans were imprisoned in a deep underground cavern at the ends of the earth, and Neptune made strong bronze gates with heavy bolts and bars to keep them down. The sea was obedient to the commands of Neptune, as we read in the story of the Great Deluge. When it was decided that Deucalion and Pyrrha were not wicked and should be saved, Neptune sent his chief Triton to blow a long twisted horn, and at the blast the sea receded to its rightful sphere.

Discovery of Neptune

The planet Neptune was 'discovered' before it was seen, if we may use an expression which seems a contradiction in terms. Mathematicians were disturbed to find that Uranus was not keeping closely to its scheduled place. For many years it was ahead of the place where calculations showed that it should be, and then after 1822 it was behind the scheduled position. Mathematicians are very loth to admit that their computations are in error, and they naturally suspected that the erratic movements of Uranus were due to a disturbing body which they could not see. Unknown to each other, two mathematicians started on the herculean task of computing where an outside planet would be to cause the discrepancies. One of these, John Couch Adams, a Cambridge mathematician, finished his work first and presented his results to Airy, the Astronomer Royal, in September, 1845, hoping that he would search the part of the heavens where

Adams believed the suspected planet existed. Unfortunately, Airy was not greatly impressed with the work of Adams and when he wrote and asked for certain details regarding the error in the position of Uranus, Adams did not reply.

Meanwhile Le Verrier, a French astronomer and mathematician, had been working on the same problem, and in the summer of 1846 he communicated three important papers to the French Academy on the subject. Airy saw some of the preliminary figures and was so impressed with their general resemblance to those given by Adams in the previous September, that he thought a telescopic search should be made for the planet. He did not consider that there was an instrument at Greenwich sufficiently large to detect the object and asked Challis at Cambridge to search for it with the Northumberland telescope. Challis agreed to do so but, as he had no chart of the part of the sky where the planet was supposed to be, he was forced to adopt a tedious method for the search which implied considerable delay.

Le Verrier sent his results to Galle at Berlin, and Galle received the letter on September 23, 1846, a year after Adams had called at the Royal Observatory to see Airy, who, unfortunately, was not at home at the time. Galle searched the same evening and found the planet in its predicted place. It is sad to relate that on August 4 and also eight days later Challis had recorded the position of the planet, but did not recognize it.

It is remarkable that the orbit assigned to Neptune by both Adams and Le Verrier is very different from its actual orbit. Both started by assuming that the planet would be at the distance from the sun which was suggested by Bode's law (see page 74), but Neptune does not conform to Bode's law which would place it 39 astronomical units from the sun, whereas its distance is only 30 astronomical units. For this reason some asserted that it was a pure coincidence that the planet was found in its predicted place, but this view of the matter is not correct. Although the planet was not nearly as far from the sun as Adams and Le Verrier believed, it is agreed that the general direction in which the disturbing body (Neptune) should be sought could be obtained with the approximate distance assumed by the two mathematicians.

Atmosphere of Neptune

Little is known about the physical features of Neptune, and as its average density is low, about 1·27, it is probable that its apparent size is due to clouds of great depth. Its atmosphere consists of methane, and its rate of rotation, measured by the spectroscope, is about 16 hours. Its one satellite revolves in a retrograde orbit. This satellite enables the astronomer to find the mass of Neptune very accurately. The planet is too far away to be seen with the naked eye.

Pluto

Pluto was the king of the underworld, a dark, gloomy place where people were supposed to go after they died. It is related how Eurydice went down to this dark underworld after she had died from the effects of the cobra's bite, and how Orpheus decided that he would go down there too and play on his lyre before Pluto, hoping that he would release

Eurydice. Pluto agreed to let her go on condition that Orpheus had sufficient faith to believe that Eurydice was following him, and so he must not look back until he reached the upper air. Unfortunately, Orpheus looked back just as he was reaching the familiar world, and then he saw Eurydice, who was following him, fading away and sinking into the underworld. He had broken the condition imposed by Pluto, and so Eurydice was compelled to return to the shades.

Discovery of Pluto

In some ways the discovery of Pluto resembled that of Neptune, though the search for Pluto was very much longer than that for Neptune. After the discovery of Neptune it was found that there were slight discrepancies in the motion of both Neptune and Uranus. Lowell's determination of the orbit of the supposed planet outside Neptune, in 1915, was based on the perturbations which it produced on Uranus. W. H. Pickering's work was largely based on the perturbations produced on Neptune. Many years of search proved fruitless but on March 13, 1930, the Lowell Observatory announced the discovery of the new planet in the constellation of Gemini. It is a curious coincidence that the date corresponded with that of Herschel's discovery of Uranus, also in Gemini, and with the anniversary of Lowell's birthday. Pluto was detected on photographs taken with the 13-inch camera which had been specially designed for searching for the planet, and the honour of the discovery fell to Tombaugh. The first two letters of Pluto are very appropriately the initials of Percival Lowell, who founded the Lowell Observatory, and whose calculations led to the search for the planet.

Pluto is a faint object, appearing as a star of magnitude 15, and has a yellowish hue. If it has a satellite it is too small to be detected with the most powerful telescope, and the planet itself is so far away that it is impossible to measure its diameter accurately. It is considered to be one of the smaller planets—probably about the size of Mars. It is impossible to measure its period of axial rotation owing to the difficulty in identifying any surface markings.

At many of the great observatories the programme does not allow any time to be devoted to the study of planetary features, and very valuable work in this branch is carried out by amateur astronomers. Not only in the study of planetary features are amateur astronomers distinguished ; many of them do excellent work in observing lunar markings, solar spots and prominences, variable stars, meteors and comets, and some are able to provide accurate data regarding the positions of comets, from which it is possible to compute orbits, while others are highly skilled in abstruse computational work.

The Asteroids

The asteroids, or minor planets, move in orbits between those of Mars and Jupiter and, with the exception of Vesta, they are all invisible to the naked eye. Bode's law seems to require that a planet should exist at a distance of about 2·8 astronomical units from the sun, and astronomers in Europe made an organized attempt to discover this planet, each observatory being assigned a certain portion of the sky in which a search was to be conducted. On January 1, 1801, Piazzi, an astronomer

at Palermo, discovered a small body in the position that had been anticipated, and the name Ceres was given to this minor planet. (Ceres was the
goddess of all that grows out of the earth, and her home was the valley
of Enna in Sicily.) When the distance of the body was known its diameter
was easily determined and was found to be 480 miles. The discovery of
such a small planet stimulated further search for others and in the
following year Olbers discovered another one to which the name Pallas

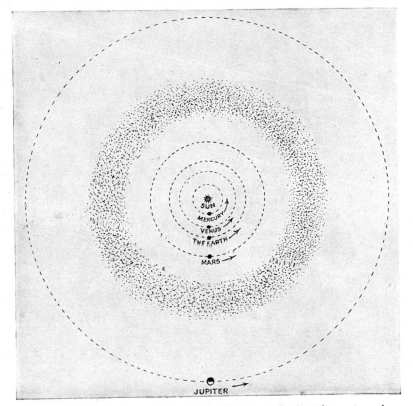

Fig. 30. The orbits of the planets from Mercury to Jupiter, drawn to scale,
and also the orbits of the minor planets or asteroids. Many of the latter
move in very eccentric orbits and also in orbits with high inclinations to the
ecliptic, but these are not shown in the diagram.

was given. Juno was discovered in 1804 and Vesta in 1807 and then an
interval of thirty-eight years elapsed before any more were found. An
amateur astronomer named Hencke spent 15 years searching for a minor
planet and at last in 1845 his efforts were rewarded by the discovery of
the fifth of these small bodies to which the name Astraea was given.

Since 1847 every year has added to the list of asteroids. In 1891 Wolf
at Heidelberg substituted photography for visual methods in the search
for these bodies. Plates are exposed for a few hours in large cameras
which are mounted equatorially and driven by clockwork so that they
point to the same part of the sky, the clockwork compensating for the

earth's rotation. When the plates are developed the stars appear as dots (if the clockwork is stopped they appear as trails owing to the earth's rotation), but as an asteroid has a motion of its own round the sun, it will appear as a short streak on the plate. Fig. 30 shows the paths of these bodies and also of the other planets as far out as Jupiter.

About 2,000 asteroids are now known and the number increases every year. Probably 100,000 of these tiny bodies exist but their total mass is very small. A rough idea of the combined mass of the bodies can be obtained as follows :

Imagine that the average diameter of the asteroids is 20 miles, which is certainly excessive, and that their average density is the same as that of the earth, which is also probably excessive. As 20 miles is 1/400th the earth's diameter and the volumes of spheres vary as the cubes of their diameters, the total volume of 100,000 asteroids would be 100,000 $(\frac{1}{400})^3$, or 1/640 of the earth's volume. Assuming the same average density for the asteroids and the earth, their mass would be only 1/640 that of the earth. This is the maximum estimate and the combined mass is probably much less. Stroobant's estimate is one-third of the above figures.

Orbits of the Asteroids

The asteroids do not all move in such approximately circular orbits as the planets nor do they all move close to the plane of the ecliptic, though none so far discovered has retrograde motion. Hidalgo is nearly five times as far from the sun at the greatest as at the least distance, and the orbit of this asteroid is inclined at 43° to the plane of the ecliptic. Within comparatively recent times some of the very small asteroids, only a few miles in diameter, have passed close to the earth, but the probability of a collision occurring is very remote. If even a small asteroid did strike the earth there would be a considerable amount of devastation—very much greater than that produced by the Siberian meteorite of 1908 (see page 112).

Origin of the Asteroids

The origin of the asteroids, like that of the planets in general, is puzzling. On first appearance it might seem that Jupiter disrupted a small planet which was moving in an orbit somewhere close to the mean orbit of the asteroids. As the Roche Limit for Jupiter is less than 100,000 miles from the centre of the planet this view is untenable. A more probable view would be that the attraction of Jupiter prevented diffuse matter scattered about in the region of the asteroids from condensing into one solid body, allowing only small condensations, but there are objections to this view also. The explosion of a planet has been suggested as a possible explanation, and the fact that a few of the asteroids reflect the light of the sun more strongly at some times than at others, thus indicating that they may not be spherical, seems to support this view. It must be admitted, however, that there is a lot of speculation in the various theories and that it is impossible to say how the asteroids originated.

Planetary Data

Name		Distance from Sun in Millions of Miles. Minimum	Mean	Maximum	Period of Revolution in Years	Period of Rotation d. h. m.
Mercury	..	28·6	36·0	43·4	0·241	88 0 0
Venus ..	..	66·8	67·3	67·7	0·615	30 0 0?
Earth ..	..	91·45	93·0	94·56	1·000	0 23 56
Mars ..	..	126·2	141·7	157·2	1·881	0 24 37
Jupiter	..	460·5	483·9	507·3	11·862	0 9 50
Saturn	..	837·8	887·2	935·6	29·458	0 10 14
Uranus	..	1700·0	1784·0	1868·2	84·015	0 10 45
Neptune	..	2768·8	2797·0	2825·2	164·788	0 15 48
Pluto ..	..	2758·0	3670·0	4582·0	247·697	?

		Diameter in Miles		Density if Water is the Unit	Mass in Terms of the Earth's Mass
Sun	..	..	864,000	1·41	333,434
Moon	..	..	2,160	3·34	0·0123
Mercury	..	..	3,000	3·73	0·0370
Venus	..	..	7,600	5·21	0·8260
Earth	..	..	7,927 7,900	5·52	1·0000
Mars	..	..	4,200	3·94	0·10860
Jupiter	..	..	88,700 82,800	1·34	318·4
Saturn	..	..	75,100 67,200	0·69	95·2
Uranus	..	..	30,900	1·36	14·6
Neptune	..	..	33,000	1·32	17·3
Pluto	..	..	?	?	?

In the case of the earth, Jupiter and Saturn, the polar diameters are given in the figures in the third column, 7,900, etc.

The mass of the earth is nearly 6×10^{21} tons and the mass of any of the other bodies can be obtained by multiplying this number by the figures in the last column of the second table.

Planetary Data (continued)

	Inclination of Orbit to Ecliptic	Inclination of Equator to Orbit	Surface Gravity Earth = 1	Orbital Velocity in Miles per Sec.	Velocity of Escape in Miles per Sec.
Mercury ..	7° 00′ 13·3″	?	0·26	29·7	2·4
Venus ..	3 23 38·7	?	0·90	21·7	6·5
Earth ..		23° 26′ 47·65″	1·00	18·47	7·0
Mars ..	1 51 00·1	23 30	0·38	15·0	3·2
Jupiter ..	1 18 22·5	3 07	2·64	8·1	38
Saturn ..	2 29 26·0	26 45	1·13	6·0	23
Uranus ..	0 46 22·6	98	0·96	4·2	14
Neptune ..	1 46 30·2	29	1·00	3·4	15
Pluto ..	17 08′ 35·3	?	?	2·9	?
Sun ..			28		392
Moon ..	5 09		0·16		1·5

The inclination of the earth's equator to the ecliptic is given for the beginning of 1944. It is decreasing at the rate of less than half a second of arc each year. In the case of the other planets the figures are given to the nearest minute of arc except for Uranus and Neptune, where they are given to the nearest degree. It is impossible to determine the amount of this inclination in the case of planets with interrogation marks.

Surface gravity on any of the bodies can be obtained by multiplying 32·2 by the number opposite the body. Thus, in the case of the sun it is 32·2 × 28 = 902 ft./sec. per sec.

Temperatures on the Planets

The temperatures on the planets and also on the moon are given in the following table. The second column gives the temperature as measured by means of the bolometer or the thermocouple. The third column gives the maximum temperature on the sunlight face on the assumption that the same face is turned towards the sun all the time. The fourth column gives the average temperatures on the assumption that there is no diurnal variation of temperature. It will be seen that there is good agreement, on the whole, between the figures in columns two and three.

Planetary Temperatures

	Measured	Calculated	
Mercury (mean, sunlight side) ..	400° C.	358° C.	172° C.
Venus (bright side)	55	191	54
Venus (dark side) ..	—20	—	—
Earth	14	119	4
Moon (centre of sunlight side) ..	120		
Moon (centre of dark side)	—150	119	4
Mars (hottest portions)	20	43	—51
Jupiter (average)	—140	—100	—151
Saturn (average)	—155	—145	—183
Uranus (average)	—180	—184	—210
Neptune		—201	—222
Pluto		—211	—229

These figures are taken from Sir Harold Spencer Jones's work, *Life on Other Worlds*, 1940, page 76, but columns three and four have been interchanged. Some of the figures differ a little from those derived on pages 75–8, but the theoretical results cannot be considered absolutely rigorous for various reasons stated in the text. In addition, there are small fluctuations in the value of the solar constant which modify the results to a slight extent.

Data for the Satellites

Planet		Satellite	Mean Distance from Planet in Miles	Diameter in Miles	Period of Revolution		
					d	h	m
Earth ..		Moon	238,857	2,160	27	7	43
Mars ..		Phobos	5,800	10 ?	0	7	39
		Deimos	14,600	5 ?	1	6	18
Jupiter ..	V	Unnamed	112,600	100 ?	0	11	57
	I	Io	261,800	2,300	1	18	28
	II	Europa	416,600	2,000	3	13	14
	III	Ganymede	664,200	3,200	7	3	43
	IV	Callisto	1,168,700	3,200	16	16	32
	VI		7,114,000	100 ?	250	16	
	VII		7,292,000	40 ?	260	1	
	VIII*		14,600,000	40 ?	739		
	IX*		15,000,000	20 ?	745		
	X		7,192,000		254	5	
	XI*		14,027,000		692	12	
Saturn	I	Mimas	115,000	400 ?		22	37
	II	Enceladus	148,000	500 ?	1	8	53
	III	Tethys	183,000	800 ?	1	21	18
	IV	Dione	234,000	700 ?	2	17	41
	V	Rhea	327,000	1,100 ?	4	12	25
	VI	Titan	759,000	2,600	15	22	41
	VII	Hyperion	930,000	300 ?	21	6	38
	VIII	Iapetus	2,210,000	1,000 ?	79	7	56
	IX	Phoebe*	8,034,000	200 ?	550		
Uranus		Ariel*	119,000	600 ?	2	12	29
		Umbriel*	165,900	400 ?	4	3	28
		Titania*	272,000	1,000 ?	8	16	56
		Oberon*	364,000	900 ?	13	11	7
Neptune		Triton*	220,000	3,000 ?	5	21	3

Where no figures are given for the diameters the satellites are so small that it is difficult to give even approximate results. Where question marks occur the figures for the diameters are only approximately correct. The three zeros after most of the diameters imply that the diameters can be considered accurate only to within about 500 miles.

CHAPTER VII

COMETS, METEORS AND THE ZODIACAL LIGHT

The word comet is derived from the Greek *koma*, a hair, and comets were believed by primitive people to be hairy stars or rather stars with long hairy tails. Aristotle believed that comets were exhalations from the earth and that such exhalations caught fire in the upper regions of the atmosphere. In ancient times comets were regarded as omens of evil and in many cases they caused panics amongst the more superstitious people.

* Denotes retrograde orbits.

The appearance of Halley's Comet in A.D. 66 was an omen to the Jews that disaster to Jerusalem was imminent, and when it appeared in 1066 it was regarded as a warning of the conquest of England by William, Duke of Normandy. Defoe tells us about the alarm in London in the early days of the plague of 1665 because a bright comet had appeared some weeks earlier. Before the Great Fire of London another comet appeared which was described as 'bright and sparkling' and many regarded it as portending a sudden and fiery judgment. In modern times the superstitious dread has practically disappeared but there is still the dread amongst some that a comet may some day collide with the earth and end the existence of our planet and all life on it as well. While such a fear is not absolutely baseless, it is usually exaggerated, and the probability of a comet producing such devastating results, even if it collided with the earth, is very small.

Orbits of Comets

Comets are members of the solar system just as much as the planets are, but the paths that they describe round the sun are usually very different from those described by the planets. In most cases comets come fairly close to the sun and then go out to an enormous distance, taking a long time—sometimes centuries—to reach their greatest distance from the sun before they start again on their return journey. Their orbits differ from those of planets in degree only, not in kind, these orbits being ellipses with high eccentricities, as a rule. In some cases the eccentricity exceeds unity, when the orbit is hyperbolic, but this happens only when the comets are disturbed by the attractions of the planets—the major planets especially and in particular by the giant planet Jupiter. A parabolic orbit is found only if the eccentricity is unity, and this happens very rarely. There are a few comets with fairly small eccentricities something like that of Pluto. When we speak of a small eccentricity it is implied that it is small for a comet, though the same eccentricity would be large in the case of a planet. Some of the minor planets have eccentricities that are larger than those of a number of comets.

There is one important feature about the orbit of comets that distinguishes them from planets—their motion is not always direct. In fact, about half the comets move in direct orbits and half in retrograde orbits, and the inclinations of their orbits to the plane of the ecliptic vary from practically 0° to 180°. This fact proves very puzzling to the cosmogonist when he attempts to explain the origin of the bodies in the solar system, of which the comets must be considered a part, and no really satisfactory explanation has yet been given regarding the retrograde motion of comets.

Composition of Comets

The portion of a comet which is often most visible and also most terrifying—the tail—is actually the most harmless. There are three quite distinct parts of a comet. The *nucleus* consists of an immense number of small particles, some not much larger than specks of dust, and varying through intermediate stages to larger particles many yards across. The nucleus never consists of one solid body—like a minor planet or a small satellite, with which its mass is comparable—a fact which explains the association between comets and meteors, which will be dealt with in the next section. Surrounding the nucleus is the *coma*, a foggy-looking disc

which enables the astronomer to distinguish a comet from a star or a minor planet. The coma, which is gaseous, varies very much in size, being hundreds of thousands of miles across in some cases and in others very much smaller. It is caused by the heat of the sun acting on the nucleus and as a consequence gases are exuded by the loose agglomeration of matter in the nucleus.

Various gases have been recognized by the use of the spectroscope, such as carbon monoxide, cyanogen, and when closer to the sun the gases of metals, sodium, iron, nickel, etc. As these gases are exuded by the heat of the sun they stream away from the nucleus but are continually replaced so that the coma remains visible in spite of the fact that the gases are being driven off. They carry along with them small particles like dust from the nucleus, and the sunlight then exercises a remarkable effect on the coma. It has been shown that the effect of light repulsion exceeds that of the sun's gravitational attraction in the case of particles with diameters of the order 1μ, where μ is the millionth of a metre, known as a *micron*. If the density of the matter is the same as that of water the two forces balance when the diameter is $1\cdot5\mu$, and if the diameter is $0\cdot16\mu$ the force of light-repulsion is 19 times that of the gravitational pull. Modifications are introduced according to the density and also the absorbing power of the material. The dust particles of various diameters are, therefore, repelled by the light pressure of the sun, and molecules of gas entangled in the dust are carried off and form the *tail* which, owing to light repulsion, is directed away from the sun. This explains why the tails of comets usually increase in size as the comets approach the sun, and in some cases the tails are hundreds of millions of miles long. We see the tail partly through the light reflected by its particles and gaseous molecules, and partly through the glowing gas, irrespective of the sun's reflected light. When we come to deal with nebulæ we shall see that a similar phenomenon occurs with them also. Fig. 31 shows Morehouse's Comet, photographed in 1908 at the Royal Observatory, Greenwich.

Owing to the extremely rarefied condition of the gases in the tail of a comet there is no danger if the earth should pass through the tail, and, indeed, this has taken place on several occasions without the slightest ill-effect. On May 19, 1910, the earth passed through the edge of the tail of Halley's Comet, which was estimated to be about 19 million miles long at the time. No traces of the effects of entering the tail were detected with certainty, though some effects may have escaped notice owing to the strong moonlight at the time. A peculiar phosphorescence of the sky was noticed when the earth passed through the tail of a comet in 1861. Alarmist reports about the danger of being poisoned by cyanogen in the tail of a comet should be discredited because, as previously remarked, the extremely attenuated condition of the gases in the tail, however dangerous such gases might be under ordinary terrestrial conditions, renders them absolutely innocuous.

Mass of a Comet

Practically all the mass of a comet is concentrated in the nucleus and the mass of this is very small in comparison with that of any of the planets. It has been estimated that the least mass of the nucleus of Halley's Comet is 30 million tons and the greatest mass is 10^{16} tons. There is a wide range

between these estimates but even with the greater mass this is only comparable with that of a minor planet. The number of grammes in 10^{16} tons is approximately 10^{22}, and if r cm. is the radius of a body with this mass, then, assuming that its density is 5, we have the relation

$$\tfrac{4}{3} \times 5\pi r^3 = 10^{22}, \text{ from which } r^3 = 478 \times 10^{18}, \text{ or } r = 7 \cdot 8 \times 10^6 \text{ cm.}$$

The diameter of a body of mass equal to that of the nucleus of Halley's Comet, if the density of the body is 5, is, therefore, about 160 kilometres or

Fig. 31.   Morehouse's Comet, photographed on November 19, 1908, by Melotte and Davidson at the Royal Observatory, Greenwich. The coma and tail are well shown in the photograph, and the main tail has a number of different sheaves. The light pressure exercised by the sun on the minute particles composing the tail of a comet is responsible for driving the tail away from the sun.

100 miles and is comparable in size with some of the minor planets. This does not imply that the nucleus is ever only 100 miles across because, as we have seen, the nucleus consists of a loose agglomeration of particles of different sizes. The space occupied by the nucleus of a comet varies with its distance from the sun, diminishing as the comet approaches the sun. At the last return of Halley's Comet the diameter of the nucleus on September 12, 1909, was 6,000 miles ; on December 13 it was 5,600 miles ; on February 4, 1910, it was 5,500 miles ; on May 9 it was 1,000

miles ; and on May 22 it was 300 miles. The diameter of the coma on the first of these dates was 13,000 miles and on the last date it had increased to 194,000 miles, but it attained its maximum size on December 14 when its diameter was 220,000 miles.

If we assume the maximum value for the mass of the nucleus given

Fig. 32. This photograph of a meteor shows that its brilliance varies at different points of its path. Towards the end of its flight, at the top of the photograph, there was a short revival of incandescence. Photography supplies the astronomer with very accurate positions of the path of a meteor, but unfortunately it is difficult to secure many photographs of meteors.

above we can form some idea of the average density of the matter composing it when the nucleus was only 300 miles across. (This occurred more than a month after the comet had made its closest approach to the sun.) We have seen that a solid body of density 5 and diameter 100 miles would correspond in mass to the nucleus, and as 300 is 3 times 100, the average density would have been $5/3^3 = 0 \cdot 2$ approximately. This shows that even with the highest concentration of the nucleus the constituent particles must have been separated a little.

Origin of Comets

The origin of comets still remains a problem. It has been suggested that some of them at least were ejected by the larger planets, Jupiter and Saturn especially. Another suggestion is that they were thrown out by the sun during a period of great activity on his surface. According to the tidal theory of the origin of the solar system comets are the remains of debris torn out of the sun by a passing star, but as this theory is open to serious objections, it cannot be accepted as an explanation of the origin of the comets. Objections have been urged against the first two theories also and indeed against others advanced to explain how comets came to move in their present orbits, and the problem still awaits solution.

Computation of a Comet's Orbit

When three observations of a comet have been made it is possible to compute its orbit, provided sufficient time has elapsed between the observations. At least a day must pass between each observation to obtain reliable data for an orbit, but even in this case the orbit which is computed is only very approximate and it is necessary to have observations separated by weeks to obtain reliable results. When this has been done, the mathematical astronomer can tell where the comet will be at any future date, and observers can set their telescopes on the predicted places and follow the comet for some time—until it becomes too faint to be seen. New comets are always appearing, on an average four or five a year, and their orbits are computed as soon as good observations of their positions are available. Some of them are found to have very long periods— perhaps requiring many hundreds of years to complete their circuit round the sun—and others have comparatively short periods, from a few years upwards. Halley's Comet is the best example of one which has often returned and whose return, known with great accuracy, has been awaited with much interest. The first authentic observation was in 240 B.C. and its average period is about 76 years.

Astronomers know when to expect a certain number of these *periodic comets*, but of course they can never predict the appearance of a *new comet*. It just comes and is seen if observers are lucky, but for every one of these unexpected comets discovered there must be a large number unobserved. They come near the sun and the earth as they sweep along on their journey round the sun, sometimes approaching the sun within a few million miles and at other times they are well over 100 million miles away. They also come close to the earth at times, in several cases within some millions of miles, when they are very likely to be detected, and in other cases hundreds of millions of miles away, when they may escape discovery. Many comets have been discovered when astronomers were engaged on other work ; they just happened to be in the part of the heavens towards which the telescope was directed or towards which the observer was looking with the naked eye. Amateur astronomers have the credit of discovering a number of comets.

Meteors

Every reader has seen 'shooting stars' but perhaps every reader is not aware of the fact that these bodies have nothing to do with the stars

and are merely tiny specks of matter, often no larger than grains of sand. Not only are the planets and comets describing orbits round the sun ; in addition, there are almost innumerable small particles which are moving round the sun in orbits similar to those of the comets, that is, with various eccentricities and at different inclinations to the plane of the ecliptic. Every day hundreds of millions of these small specks encounter the earth's atmosphere and, owing to their speed, develop a considerable amount of heat and are burnt up without reaching the surface of the earth. Occasionally a large meteor strikes the atmosphere and is not completely consumed, only the outer portions of its surface being scorched, and it strikes the ground, being then known as a *meteorite*. Fig. 32 shows a photograph of a fairly bright meteor in flight.

Relation between Comets and Meteors

There is a close connection between comets and meteors, though it would be incorrect to say that all meteors are associated with comets or that all comets are responsible for meteors. There are well-known meteor showers which are definitely connected with certain comets, and in this connection the story of Biela's Comet is very interesting.

Biela's Comet revolved round the sun in about $6\frac{3}{4}$ years and had been observed on various occasions before 1845 when it was seen to split into two parts. When it returned in 1852 these two parts had separated considerably, being over a million miles apart, and it was impossible to tell which was the original larger one seen in 1845. In September of that year the comets disappeared from view and from that time were never seen again. Although Biela's Comet had vanished from sight its after-effects remained for many years and to a very small extent still remain. In 1872, when it was expected to return, there took place a most wonderful display of meteors on November 27, and since then the shower has been repeated about the same date, sometimes as a rich shower, sometimes as a feeble display, though in recent years it has been very feeble or in some cases non-existent. The debris of Biela's Comet had encountered the earth's atmosphere and had been responsible for a fine display of meteors. It is interesting to notice that, in spite of the enormous number of meteors which appeared, not one, so far as is known, struck the ground, and this would have happened if the bodies composing the nucleus of the comet had been fairly large—say, as large as a cricket ball. It appears, therefore, that the nucleus of Biela's Comet must have consisted of small particles, and probably the same remark applies to most of the other comets.

Just as Biela's Comet was responsible for a rich meteoric display in 1872, so Tempel's Comet was responsible for fine displays in 1799, 1833 and also in 1866, though Tempel's Comet did not break up as Biela's Comet did. The Leonid meteor shower, due to the debris of Tempel's Comet, appears on November 13 and 14, but in recent times it has become a very weak shower in comparison with some of its previous displays. There are at least eight meteor showers associated with comets, and perhaps some of the other meteor showers are the debris of comets which broke up many centuries ago, their nuclei still continuing to follow the old orbits and becoming dispersed along the tracks so that the earth runs into them at the same time each year. (See Fig. 33.)

Radiants and Real Paths of Meteors

When the paths of meteors which belong to some of the well-estab-lished showers are traced backwards, they seem to converge to a point, or at least to a small area in the sky, to which the name *radiant* is given.

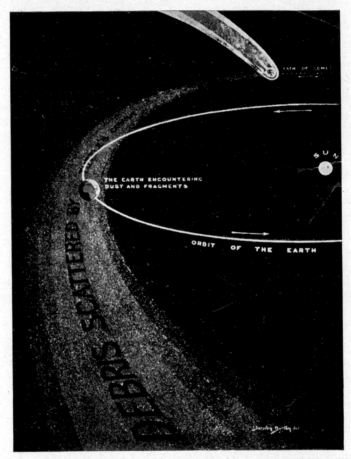

Fig. 33. A comet discards a certain amount of its matter as it moves round the sun, and meteoric debris is spread out along its orbit, this debris continuing to revolve round the sun just as Saturn's rings revolve round the planet. The earth encounters this debris on certain occasions and a shower of meteors results from the encounter. The debris cannot be seen unless it encounters the earth's atmosphere, and then it appears only as flashes of light from the particles becoming incandescent.

The meteors are actually moving in parallel lines and their apparent divergence from a small area is an effect of perspective. The same effect is produced when we look at a straight length of railway track, the rails appearing to meet at a great distance from the eye. If we could imagine a number of rails, at various distances apart, and all parallel, the same effect would be produced, and we could apply the name *radiant* to the

point where they appeared to converge, if we wished to adopt astronomical nomenclature, though the term *vanishing point* is better understood.

When the same meteor is seen by two or more observers who are separated by 30 or 40 miles at least, and each records its apparent path with reference to the stars, it is possible to find its height at the beginning and end of its flight, the part of the earth over which it moved, and also its velocity, provided its time of flight can be accurately recorded. This last part of the observer's work is often the most difficult because in many cases the time during which a meteor makes itself visible is a matter of only a second or two, and sometimes merely the fraction of a second.

The principle of finding the height and path of a meteor is the same as that used by the surveyor with a base line and two angles, as already described (see page 56) but the work is a little more complicated as the astronomer is working in three dimensions. In addition, sometimes the observers miss a part of the path of the meteor, or one observer sees the meteor before the other observer. A short description of a method for finding the 'true path' of a meteor is given in Appendix V.

Meteorites

Meteorites are comparatively rare in this country but are frequently picked up in America, not because they have any special preference for falling there, but because more will naturally occur in the much larger area. In most cases meteorites are accompanied by a loud noise and a sound like an explosion, and frequently the body breaks up into a number of small portions which may be scattered over a large area. When these are picked up and analysed they are found to contain the same elements as those existing on the earth, iron, nickel, calcium, magnesium, manganese, chromium, sodium, aluminium, etc. Sometimes there are 'stony' meteorites which belong to a class of rocks low in silicic acid but high in basic constituents—iron and magnesia. Peary, of North Pole fame, brought three large meteorites from Greenland to America in 1895 and 1897, and they are now in the Natural History Museum, New York City. The largest weighs 36½ tons and its approximate dimensions are 10·9 × 6·8 × 5·2 feet. It would require many pages to describe all the meteorites which have been picked up in every part of the world and we shall finish this portion by describing two very large ones of considerable interest. Fig. 34 shows a meteorite of metallic composition, which weighs more than half a ton.

Near Cañon Diabolo in Arizona there is a crater in the desert, 570 feet deep and 4,200 feet in diameter, which is due to the impact of a meteorite. Meteoric iron has been picked up within a radius of six miles from the crater, and these pieces, aggregating several tons in weight, were once associated with the great mass which now lies buried in the earth. It is impossible to say when the meteorite fell but certain limits for the time can be set by two considerations. On the rim of the crater there are cedar trees which are about 700 years old, so the crater must have been formed before the trees started their growth. From the weathering of the rocks it is thought that the fall of the meteorite could not have occurred more than 5,000 years ago, and it may have happened any time between these limits.

On June 30, 1908, a meteorite fell in a forest in north central Siberia and devastated a large area—three or four thousand square miles. Partly

owing to the war of 1914–18 very little was known of this fall until 1927 when Kulik, of the Russian Academy of Science, led an expedition to the place to collect information. He found that the trees had been blown down all round the place of the fall, for a radius of about 30 miles, and their tops were pointing away from the centre. For a distance of 10 miles from the centre the scorching effects of the hot air were noticed, and for 15 miles the rush of air had been sufficiently strong to break the trees. Some of the natives informed Kulik that the fall was accompanied by a sound

Fig. 34.   A meteorite weighing 1,400 pounds, found in Otumpa, Mexico. This meteorite is composed largely of iron and the name siderolite (from the Greek *sideros*, iron, and *lithos*, a stone) is applied to this class of meteorite. Many meteorites consist largely of non-metallic substances, containing silicates and other stony substances.

louder than thunder, and that a column of fire and smoke had shot up, spreading rapidly as a dark cloud in all directions.

The fire-marked region, which is swampy country, had a number of wide funnel-shaped craters, only a few feet deep, the largest of them being 150 feet in diameter. The meteorite probably broke up into small pieces before striking the ground, but only minute portions of the debris of the body have been found. It was believed that the meteorite was a part of the nucleus of Comet Pons-Winnecke which makes a fairly close approach to the earth's orbit, but this view is now discredited because the meteorite was moving in a different direction from that of the comet. It is fortunate that such falls are very rare. If any of these large meteorites fell in a populous district there would be terrible devastation and loss of life.

H

The Zodiacal Light

In northern latitudes after nightfall in the spring the *zodiacal light* is seen in the west and before dawn in the autumn in the east. A clear moonless sky is necessary to see the phenomenon. Near the horizon it is seen

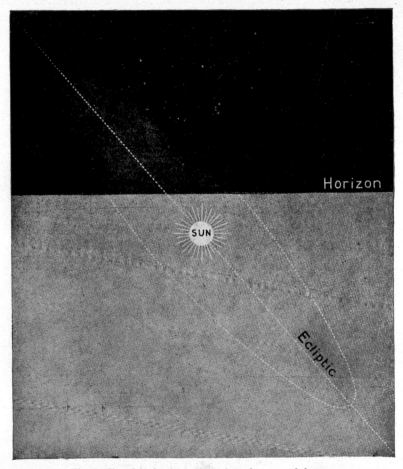

Fig. 35. The zodiacal light is supposed to be caused by an enormous number of very minute particles moving round the sun near the plane of the ecliptic. When the ecliptic is inclined to the horizon at a fairly large angle the zodiacal light is seen well above the horizon.

broadest and brightest and it tapers upwards to about 90° from the sun, following the course of the ecliptic. In the tropics the zodiacal light is seen at its best, and is visible there throughout the year. The ecliptic is more nearly perpendicular to the horizon in tropical regions than it is in places of higher latitudes and hence, as the zodiacal light lies close to the ecliptic, it attains a greater altitude and is better seen in the former case

than in the latter. Fig. 35 shows the zodiacal light when the ecliptic has a considerable inclination to the horizon.

It is believed to be sunlight reflected from myriads of small bodies or perhaps molecules of gas which are revolving round the sun very close to the ecliptic, and which extend far outside the earth's orbit. The matter in this narrow disc must be extremely diffuse because it does not appreciably retard the movements of the planets. Although other explanations for the phenomenon have been advanced, the theory just mentioned is the most probable and is generally accepted.

CHAPTER VIII

THE STARS

How Stellar Distances are Described

OUR CONSIDERATIONS UP TO THE PRESENT HAVE BEEN LARGELY LIMITED to those bodies which are members of the solar system. We saw that their distances can be expressed in miles or more conveniently in terms of an astronomical unit, the former being more suitable for the distances of the satellites from their primaries and the latter for the distances of the planets from the sun and from one another. When we leave the solar system and enter the realm of the stars neither of these units is large enough to express the distances very conveniently. In engineering work the hundredth of an inch is vitally important and must be taken into consideration. When we deal with the surveyor's measurements such a refinement would be meaningless, and distances which are given to the nearest foot or yard are often accurate enough for practical purposes. When we come to deal with greater distances still—say the distance from Liverpool to New York—we should never think of giving this distance with the surveyor's accuracy and the nearest mile or two will suffice. Planetary distances may be in error by about 1 in 1,000, so when we say that Pluto's mean distance from the sun is 3,670 million miles we are uncertain about these figures to within three or four million miles. Greater uncertainty still exists in describing stellar distances, which are not usually given in miles or even in astronomical units but in light-years, or in parallaxes or in parsecs.

A *light-year* denotes the number of miles that light will travel in a year—nearly 6×10^{12} (the other terms will be explained later). Light-years are usually given to two decimal places ; thus we speak of Proxima Centauri as being 4·16 light-years from us, and hence, even if we assume the highest accuracy with such figures, there may be an error of 0·005 light-year. Actually, owing to the difficulties inherent in the work of measuring stellar distances, the error is much greater than this, but if we accept this as the minimum error, it corresponds to a distance $0·005 \times 6 \times 10^{12} = 3 \times 10^{10}$ miles. Hence at the best we cannot express the distances of the stars with an accuracy greater than 30,000 million miles. As these figures apply to the nearest star for which the parallax (see next section) can be found much more accurately than for the more distant stars, we see how futile it would be to describe the distances of the stars as being so many million miles.

How the Distances of the Stars are measured.

We saw that a few bodies in the solar system were sufficiently close to the earth to have their distances measured by taking a base line on the earth a few thousand miles long. It was then possible to make use of the distances of these nearer bodies to find the distances of others which were more remote from the earth and sun. In measuring the distances of stars, we require a much longer base line than any distance on the earth could provide, and in fact the base line used, twice an astronomical unit, is too small for the far-away stars, though providing satisfactory results for those that are comparatively close. The principle is the same as that employed for measuring the distance of the moon, as the following explanation will show.

Imagine that we want to find the distance to a star which is assumed from its brightness to be comparatively close to us—an assumption which

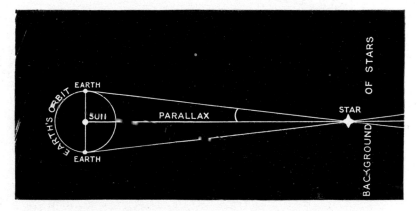

Fig. 36. Just as two positions on the earth make a base line for measuring the distance of the moon, so two positions on the earth's orbit make a base line for measuring the distance of a star. This base line is 186 million miles in length, and the angle subtended by *half* this base line, that is, the angle subtended by an astronomical unit, at the star when the line star–sun is perpendicular to the base line, is known as the parallax of the star.

is often justified. A faint star, which may be assumed to be very far away, say at an infinite distance, in comparison with the distance of the nearer star, now takes the place of any star which could be used in finding the moon's distance (see page 56). The base line is the distance between two positions of the earth in its orbit with an interval of six months, and the angle subtended at the star by this base line is found and hence the distance of the star. (Fig. 36.) The value of the angle will depend upon the positions in the earth's orbit from which the observations are made, and it will obviously be a maximum when the line joining the two positions is perpendicular to the line from the sun to the star. Half this maximum angle or the maximum angle subtended at the star by the line joining the earth and sun, is known as the *parallax* of the star. (Notice the same expression for the angle subtended at the sun by the radius of the earth.) We shall now deal with a particular case to show how the calculations are made.

The parallax of Sirius has been found to be 0·371 second, what is its distance from the earth (or sun) ?

Applying the rule previously given and adopting 1 as the length of the line joining the earth and sun, the star's distance is 206,265/0·371 = 555,970 astronomical units, or about 51·7 × 10^{12} miles. As light moves 186,271 miles per second or 5·88 × 10^{12} miles in a year, the distance of Sirius is 51·7 × 10^{12}/5·88 × 10^{12} = 8·80 light-years very nearly.

If we could imagine a star so close that its parallax was 1 second of arc, its distance would be 206,265 astronomical units or 1·92 × 10^{13} miles which is 3·258 light-years. The name *parsec* is given to a distance at which the parallax is one second. A stars distance in light-years is, therefore, 3·258/p, where p is a star's parallax in seconds.

The results can be shown in the following tabular form :

One light-year is 5·88 × 10^{12} miles or 9·46 × 10^{12} km.

One parsec is 1·92 × 10^{13} miles or 3·09 × 10^{13} km. or 3·258 light-years.

A star's distance in light-years is 3·258/p or 19·2 × 10^{12}/p miles.

The nearest star to us is Proxima Centauri whose parallax is 0·783 second. Hence its distance is 3·258/0·783 = 4·16 light-years.

In the description of the method used for determining the distance of a star it was assumed that the faint star was at an infinite distance, but this assumption is not correct. For this reason the results obtained are only the *relative parallaxes* or parallaxes with reference to some other star. If the distance of the faint star and therefore its parallax are known (and a method for finding them will be described later) the *absolute parallax* is obtained by adding a correction to the relative parallax. This correction is usually very small—a few thousandths of a second of arc.

Limits to the Accuracy of Stellar Parallaxes

Schlesinger at the Yerkes Observatory first developed the modern photographic method for finding parallaxes, about 1903, and a number of observatories are carrying out the work of stellar parallaxes so that direct parallaxes of about four thousand stars are now available. There is a limitation to the accuracy of this *trigonometrical* method because the percentage of error increases from about one for the nearest stars to ten for stars 70 light-years distant, and when a star is 160 light-years away the method is too untrustworthy to be used. Certain indirect methods are used for the more distant stars, and these will be described later.

Motions of the Stars

Although the above method seems simple so far as the theory is concerned, there are many complications which render the practical side of the work difficult. It has been assumed that the star whose parallax is to be found, as well as the faint star, are not moving, but no star in the heavens is at rest. All the stars are in motion with velocities varying from a few miles a second up to more than a hundred miles a second. Then, irrespective of this *proper motion* of the stars, the solar system itself is in motion, carrying the observer with it. Hence it is necessary to take several photographs at intervals of six months to eliminate the effects of the motions of the stars and of the sun. Reference has already been made to the effects of refraction, which, of course, can be allowed for, but it is

always advisable to reduce the refraction to the minimum. This is accomplished by selecting the times when the star is highest, because refraction is then least, and hence the photographs are taken when the star is near its meridian passage.

Proper motion is the rate of change in the position of the star on the celestial sphere and it can be measured with high accuracy by comparing two photographs of a region in the sky taken several years apart. The amount of proper motion may seem very small when measured in the number of seconds of arc described by the star each year. The largest known proper motion is only 10·25 seconds a year, and this takes place with Barnard's star discovered in 1916. It is obvious that a comparatively close star may have a large angular motion and yet may not be moving rapidly, and on the other hand a far-off star may have a small angular motion and its velocity may be high. Proper motion relates to the part of the motion that is *transverse* to the line of sight, and a star may be moving rapidly from or towards us and yet it shows no proper motion. The name *radial velocity* is applied to this latter motion which can be detected with the spectroscope.

Most readers have some knowledge of the spectroscope, but those who know nothing about it will find a short description in Appendix X. The Doppler principle supplies the necessary information for finding the line-of-sight velocity of a star, the lines in the spectrum being displaced towards the red if the star is receding from us and towards the violet if the star is approaching us. Wave-lengths are expressed in units known as angstroms, one angstrom, denoted by 1 A, being 10⁻⁸ cm. It is named after the Swedish physicist Ångström who first made accurate measurements of the wave-length of light. Lines are indicated thus, λ 6563, denoting wave-length 6563 A or 6563 × 10⁻⁸ cm. If Δ λ is the change of wave-length of a line whose wave-length is λ the radial velocity is

$$\text{Velocity of light} \times \Delta\lambda/\lambda.$$

Thus, if a line whose wave-length is 6563 A is displaced 1 A towards the red, the star is receding from us with a velocity 1/6563 that of light, or 28·4 miles a second. If the displacement is towards the violet the velocity is the same but the star is approaching us.

Radial velocities are measured by photographing the spectrum of the star in conjunction with a comparison spectrum of a laboratory source. By examining the spectrogram under the microscope the displacements of the lines are measured with reference to the comparison lines. Radial velocities of thousands of stars have been determined in this way, a number of observatories co-operating in the scheme.

Suppose that μ is the annual proper motion of a star whose parallax is *p* and of which the *tangential velocity* T in miles a second is required, the first step in the computation is to find the distance of the star. It has been shown that this is 3·258/*p* in light-years or 19·2 × 10¹²/*p* in miles. We have seen that proper motion refers to that part of the motion which is *transverse* or at *right angles* to the line of sight, and hence the length of the arc traversed by the star in a year is 19·2 μ × 10¹²/206,265 *p* miles.

Dividing this by the number of seconds in a year the result is 2·94 μ/*p* miles a second or 4·74 μ/*p* kilometres a second.

As an illustration of the application of this formula take the case of

Kapteyn's star which, next to Barnard's star, has the largest proper motion. The parallax of this star is 0·317 second and its annual proper motion is 8·76 seconds. Hence its tangential velocity is 2·94 × 8·76/0·317 =81 miles a second.

Knowing the star's radial velocity V and its tangential velocity T, its space velocity v is easily derived from the principle of the parallelogram of velocities, and is found from the formula $v^2 = V^2 + T^2$. If the direction of motion makes an angle θ with the line of sight, θ is derived from the equation tan θ $= T/V$.

It has been found that Arcturus has the highest space velocity among the brighter stars. Its radial velocity is small—only 3 miles a second in a direction away from us, but its tangential velocity is about 84 miles a second. The space velocity of this star is, therefore, $\sqrt{3^2 + 84^2}$, or 84·05 miles a second. The direction which its space motion makes with the line of sight is found from tan θ $= 84/3 = 28$, and hence θ is nearly 88°. Arcturus is therefore moving nearly at right angles to the line of sight.

One important matter must be pointed out before leaving this subject. When the spectroscope determines the radial velocity of a star the orbital velocity of the earth is necessarily involved in assisting with the displacements of the lines in the spectrum of the star, and hence the velocity obtained would include the earth's orbital velocity. This is easily allowed for, and in practice the observed radial velocities of stars are referred to the *sun*, not to the earth. If they were referred to the earth the radial velocities in certain cases might vary by nearly 37 miles a second, twice the earth's orbital velocity, because the earth might be approaching the star at one time and receding from it six months later.

Aberration

Aberration was discovered by Bradley and explained by him in 1727. Owing to its effect the direction of a star keeps changing slightly throughout the year. It is due to the fact that the *apparent* direction of the light from any star is the resultant of the velocity of light and of the velocity of the earth. A familiar illustration is found when we hold an umbrella to protect ourselves from rain, which we can imagine, for the present purpose, to fall quite vertically. If we stand still we hold the umbrella straight overhead, but if we are moving it will be necessary to hold the umbrella inclined in the direction of motion. This is because the *apparent* direction in which the rain is falling is then inclined to the vertical, though not its real direction, and the faster we move the greater the slope at which we must hold the umbrella. If we could imagine someone ascending in a lift which was open at the top, it would be unnecessary for him to slope his umbrella to protect himself from the rain. This is because he is *moving in the same direction as the rain*. The same effect would be noticed if a strong wind drove the rain horizontally ; in this case whether we moved or stood still the umbrella would have to point horizontally or in the direction of the rainfall, to protect us.

The light from a star can be taken to represent the rain and the orbital motion of the earth the movement of the person with the umbrella. Suppose a star is in the pole of the ecliptic so that its light is moving at right angles to the direction of the earth's motion ; this assumption of the

position of the star is made to simplify the diagram (Fig. 37). A telescope would not be directed to the actual place of the star but to its *apparent* place, which, on the analogy of the umbrella, would be displaced forward in the direction of the earth's motion. Fig. 38 shows that the tangent of the angle of displacement is the velocity of the earth divided by the velocity of light, that is, 18·47/186,271 = 0·00009916, so that the aberration is nearly 20·5 seconds. Its value for the mean distance of the earth from the sun is usually taken as 20·47 seconds of arc. This apparent displacement of a star when the earth is moving at average speed at right angles to the star's direction, is known as the *constant of aberration*.

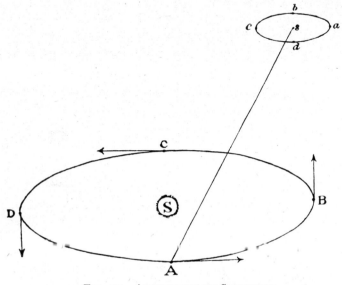

FIG. 37. ABERRATION OF STARLIGHT

Light from a star *s* reaches the earth at A, but the star does not appear to be at *s*, but at *a*, that is, it appears to be displaced in the direction of the earth's motion. As the earth continues in its motion the star appears to describe a small curve *abcd* in the heavens. This curve is a circle if the star is in the pole of the ecliptic and an ellipse on other occasions, unless it happens to lie in the plane of the ecliptic, when it is a straight line.

If the star is not in the pole of the ecliptic the value of its aberration is found as follows. Suppose a line is drawn from the earth in the direction of its orbital motion and another line is drawn from the earth to the star. The angle between these two lines is called the *earth's way*, and the amount of the aberration in seconds of arc is 20.47 sin (earth's way). See Appendix XI for a proof of this.

If the star lies in front of or behind the direction of the earth's motion this angle is zero and the aberration is also zero. If the angle is 30° the aberration is 10·23 seconds, and so on. When the star is in the pole of the ecliptic, the angle is 90° but this is not the only position in which it can be 90° and there are in theory innumerable other places which fulfil this condition.

Not only is there aberration due to the orbital velocity of the earth ;

there is also a small aberration caused by the earth's rotation. As the maximum velocity of the earth's rotation is in equatorial regions where it is about 0·015 that of the orbital velocity, the greatest aberration due to the earth's rotation is 20·47 × 0·015 = 0·3 second of arc. Aberration must be taken into consideration when the astronomer is concerned with the accurate positions of stars.

Weighing the Stars

A considerable number of stars which appear as single stars to the unaided eye are known to be *binaries*, and the stars composing the system can be seen only with the telescope. These stars are called *visual binaries* and are revolving round their common centre of gravity, just like the earth-moon system. There are also *spectroscopic binaries* which are too close to be seen with the telescope but the periodic oscillations of the lines in their spectra indicate that they are also binaries. Amongst the many important features of binary stars one of the most interesting is the method for finding their masses. Their distances can be found by the trigonometrical method previously described or by other methods, and then when their angular separation has been measured, their distance apart is easily computed. Suppose this mean distance is found to be a astro-

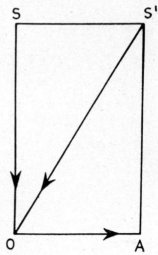

Fig. 38. Light from a star S reaches the earth at O, the direction of the light being at right angles to the direction OA of the earth's orbital motion. If SO and OA represent the velocities of light and of the earth in magnitude and direction, and the angle SOS' is a, the constant of aberration, then tan a = SS'/SO = velocity of the earth divided by the velocity of light.

nomical units and the time of a complete revolution is T years, and k is the combined mass of the stars, the mass of the sun being the unit ; then by the formula on page 72, $k = a^3/T^2$. This gives the combined mass of the system but does not inform us about the mass of each star separately. When their revolutions have been observed with reference to some neighbouring stars, or with the spectroscope, it is then possible to find their individual masses, because their relative distances from the centre of gravity of the system can be found. We saw that in the case of the earth-moon system if the barycentre is known to be 3,000 miles from the centre of the earth, or about 1/80 of the moon's distance from the centre of the earth, this shows that the earth is about 80 times as massive as the moon. The same principle is applied to determining the individual masses of binaries. One very interesting fact has come to light as a result of weighing a number of binaries—the masses of the stars, binaries included, generally lie between 0·2 and 10 times the mass of the sun. In other words, nature seems to have a preference for producing stars of masses from about 2 × 10³⁴ to 4 × 10³² grammes and seldom deviates by more than the factor 10 from the larger mass, nor scarcely ever falls below the smaller mass. The reason why she makes this choice will be explained later.

The above method cannot be applied to single stars nor can it be

applied to the great majority of visual binaries because the components of these are so far apart that T is very large. Hence a long time is required to observe the time of revolution, or at least to determine it with accuracy. But now a most important work is done when a binary system is too far off for its trigonometrical parallax to be found (see page 117) provided the period of revolution is known. An explanation of this follows.

Stellar Distances Determined by Statistical Methods

We have seen that the stars do not differ much in mass from the sun and as a first approximation we can assume that any star has a mass equal to that of the sun. Hence we can substitute 2 for k in the above equation, $k = a^3/T^2$, and thus obtain the following expression

$$a^3 = 2T^2$$

This supplies the mean distance between the stars and when the astronomer measures the angular distance he can find how far away the system is from the earth. In actual practice the parallax can be found from the simpler form

$$p^3 = a^3/2T^2, \text{ or } p = a/\sqrt[3]{2T^2} = 0 \cdot 794 \, a/\sqrt[3]{T^2}$$

if p is expressed in seconds of arc and a is also expressed in seconds of arc.* From p the distance can be obtained in light-years or parsecs by the formulæ previously given.

At first sight it may seem that considerable inaccuracies must arise in applying this method because of the uncertainty of the sum of the masses of the components of the system. The inaccuracy is not so great, however, as one might think, and this is shown from the examples that follow.

Suppose the sum of the masses is 2 ; then $p = 0 \cdot 794 \, a/\sqrt[3]{T^2}$. If the sum of the masses is 10, $p = 2 \cdot 15 \, a/\sqrt[3]{T^2}$, and the ratio of the latter to the former is $2 \cdot 7$, not a very large ratio considering the great discrepancy in the assumed masses. If the sum of the masses is 5 the value of p is $1 \cdot 710 \, a/\sqrt[3]{T^2}$ and the ratio of this to the first value is just over 2. Statistically, this method for finding parallaxes supplies most useful information. Parallaxes determined in this way are known as *dynamical parallaxes*.

* The following elementary considerations will show the validity of this formula.
Let a be the number of seconds subtended by the semi-major axis of the orbit of the binary system, the length of this semi-major axis being a astronomical units. If d is the distance of the system in astronomical units, then

$$a''/206265 = a/d$$

Also, $p = 206265/d$ (see page 57).
Dividing the first of these equations by the second,

$$a'' = pa, \text{ or } p = a''/a = a''/\sqrt[3]{2T^2}.$$

CHAPTER IX

THE STARS (*continued*)

Stellar Magnitudes

HIPPARCHUS, BORN AT BITHYNIA IN 140 B.C., WAS THE FIRST TO REDUCE astronomy to a systematic form. Before his time astronomy consisted largely in a knowledge of isolated facts, and, useful as they may have been, they were not co-ordinated into any coherent scheme. Amongst other important work in astronomy he compiled the earliest star catalogue, which included 1,081 stars, and he also divided the stars into six classes according to their brightness, including about twenty of the brightest stars in the 1st magnitude group and the hundreds of faint stars that could just be seen into the 6th magnitude group. Between these extremes stars of intermediate brightness were placed in the category of 2nd, 3rd, etc., magnitudes. It should be particularly noticed that the brighter a star is the smaller is the number denoting its magnitude, and *vice versa*.

In 1850 an English astronomer, Pogson, established a definite light ratio between stars of different magnitudes. This ratio will be easily remembered by noticing why the light ratio between a star of magnitude 1 and a star of magnitude 6 is 100. There are 5 steps between 1 and 6 and if we assume that each step corresponds to a light ratio of 2·512 we find that this ratio just fits in with the scheme, in other words, 2·512 raised to the fifth power is almost exactly 100. A star of magnitude 1 is 2·512 times as bright as a star of magnitude 2 and a star of magnitude 2 is 2·512 times as bright as one of magnitude 3, and so on. Hence a star of magnitude 1 is 2·512 × 2·512 or $2·512^2 = 6·31$ times as bright as a star of magnitude 3. A star of magnitude 2 is $2·512^4$ times as bright as one of magnitude 6 (6 − 2 = 4), or 39·8 times as bright.

Refinements in determining stellar magnitudes have necessitated the introduction of intermediate numbers which are fractional. Thus the star Spica has a magnitude 1·21 and Regulus has a magnitude 1·34. Suppose we want to find the relation between the brightness of Regulus and Spica. The relative luminosities are as $1/2·512^{1·34}$ to $1/2·512^{1·21}$ and hence the relative luminosities are as $2·512^{1·21}$ to $2·512^{1·34}$, but it is impossible to raise this number to these powers without the use of logarithms. Readers are expected to understand the use of logarithms ; those who are not conversant with their use must accept the results that follow.

Four-figure tables are more than sufficient for most of such computations, but we shall use four figures to ensure the greatest accuracy. Let l_1 and l_2 denote the relative luminosities or brightnesses of the two stars, then
$$l_1 = 2·512^{1·21}, \quad l_2 = 2·512^{1·34}$$
$$\log l_1 = 1·21 \log 2·512 = 1·21 × 0·4 = 0·484, \text{ hence } l_1 = 3·048$$
$$\log l_2 = 1·34 \log 2·512 = 1·34 × 0·4 = 0·536, \text{ hence } l_2 = 3·436$$

The ratio of l_1 to l_2 is therefore as 3·048 to 3·436 or as 1 to 1·127 or 1 to 1·13 with sufficient accuracy.

Those who are familiar with the use of indices can solve the problem

more easily by noticing that the ratio of l_1 to l_2 is simply 2·512 with 0·13 as index, 0·13 being the difference in the magnitudes. Hence the ratio is $2·512^{0·13}$, and taking logarithms we find that 0·13 log 2·512 is 0·052, the antilogarithm of which is 1·127.

Readers must not imagine from this description of magnitudes that a star of magnitude 1 is the brightest. There are twenty stars included in the category of stars of the first magnitude although they range through nearly three magnitudes. The well-known star Aldebaran is very nearly, but not quite, first magnitude, its actual magnitude being 1·06, and Sirius is considerably brighter than Aldebaran, though included among the first magnitude stars. When a star is brighter than the standard adopted for first magnitude it is necessary to denotes its magnitude by a decimal or even a negative number. Thus Procyon has a magnitude 0·48 so that its brightness compared with that of Aldebaran is 1·71. The difference in the magnitudes of the stars is 0·58, and 0·58 log 2·512 is 0·232, and the antilogarithm of this is 1·706. The magnitude of Sirius is —1·58 which is 2·06 magnitudes less than Procyon. Hence Sirius is brighter than Procyon in the ratio $2·512^{2·06} = 6·67$.

The system of assigning magnitudes is extended to the planets and also to the sun and moon. The magnitude of the sun is —26·72, so that the sun is $2·512^{27·72}$ times as bright as a star of magnitude 1 (deducting —26·72 from 1 gives 27·72). The value of $2·512^{27·72}$ is found in the usual way. If R is the ratio of the sun's luminosity to that of a 1st magnitude star, log R = 27·72 log 2·512 = 11·088. The antilogarithm of this number is $1·225 \times 10^{11}$, so that the luminosity of the sun is more than 100,000 million times that of a star of the 1st magnitude. The magnitude of full moon is —12·5, and of Venus at brightest —4·3.

Absolute Magnitudes

The term *magnitude* applies to the apparent brightness of a star and tells us nothing about its intrinsic brightness because we have not taken into consideration the distance of the star. We saw that Sirius with a magnitude —1·58 was brighter than Aldebaran with a magnitude 1·06 but to what is this difference of brightness due ? It may be due to a greater intrinsic brightness on the part of Sirius or it may be due to the fact that Sirius is nearer to us than Aldebaran, just as a feeble electric globe which is nearer us looks brighter than a stronger globe which is far off. It may interest readers to know that Aldebaran is more than six times as far away as Sirius is and if it were at the distance of Sirius it would appear brighter than this star—the brightest in the heavens. It is very important, therefore, that we should be able to compare the luminosities of stars by assuming that they are all placed at the same distance from us.

It has been agreed to give the name *absolute magnitude* to the apparent magnitude of a star if it were placed at a distance of 10 parsecs or 32·6 light-years from us. Before computing the absolute magnitude of a star it is necessary to know its distance in light-years or to know its parallax. We shall adapt the formulæ to suit both the light-year distance and the distance expressed by parallax.

The intensity of illumination falls off as the square of the distance of the illuminated surface from the source of illumination (see page 76). Suppose a star is at a distance L light-years and its luminosity is l_1 and

that it is moved to a distance 32·6 light-years where its luminosity is l_2. Obviously, we have the relation

$$\left(\frac{L}{32\cdot6}\right)^2 = \frac{l_2}{l_1}$$

Now, as we have seen, the ratio l_2 to l_1 is $2\cdot512^{(m\ m_a)}$, where m_a is the magnitude of the star at the distance 32·6 light-years, m being its apparent magnitude. Hence

$$\left(\frac{L}{32\cdot6}\right)^2 = 2\cdot512^{(m-m_a)}$$

Taking logarithms of both sides, and remembering that log 2·512 is 0·4, we obtain the relation,

$$2(\log L - \log 32\cdot6) = 0\cdot4(m-m_a)$$

Substituting 1·5132 for log 32·6 and simplifying we obtain

$$m_a = m + 7\cdot566 - 5\log L$$

If the parallax is used a less convenient formula is obtained. We have seen that L, the distance of a star in light-years, is $3\cdot26/p$, or $32\cdot6/10p$ (see page 117), and it is only necessary to substitute this value for L in the above expression. We thus obtain for log L the expression log 32·6 — log p —1. Hence

$$2(\log 32\cdot6 - \log p - 1 - \log 32\cdot6) = 0\cdot4(m-m_a), \text{ from which}$$
$$2 + 2\log p = 0\cdot4\ (m_a\text{-}m), \text{ or } m_a = m + 5 + 5\log p$$

Both these formulæ will be used to find the absolute magnitude of Sirius whose apparent magnitude is −1.58 and whose distance is 8·78 light-years or, expressed as a parallax, 0·371 second.

Using the distance in light-years first we find
$$m_a = -1\cdot58 + 7\cdot566 - 5\log 8\cdot78 = 5\cdot986\ -5\ \times 0\cdot9435 = 1\cdot27$$

If we use the parallax the formula gives
$$m_a = -1\cdot58+5+5\log 0\cdot371 = -1\cdot58+5+5\ (-1+0\cdot5694) = 1\cdot27.$$

When the parallax is used it involves the use of a logarithm of a decimal and this introduces negative numbers, as shown above, which may be confusing at times. For this reason the formula which makes use of the distance in light-years is often more convenient.

Although the determination of absolute magnitudes may not appear to have any practical value, we shall see later that it has one of the most important applications in the whole realm of astronomy in enabling the astronomer to determine the distances of very far-off stars, whose distances could not have been found with much accuracy by any other method.

Variable Stars

Up to the present it has been assumed that a star always has the same apparent magnitude but there are a great many stars whose magnitudes undergo considerable fluctuations. In some cases these fluctuations are due to internal causes—pulsation of the star or other changes—but in other

cases they are due to the influence of an external body which comes between the star and the earth, thus cutting off a portion of its light. One star in particular should be noticed because of its rapid change in brightness.

Eclipsing Binaries

Algol (β Persei) is the best-known of the *eclipsing binaries*, the name given to these stars which undergo eclipses owing to some of the light being cut off by a revolving companion. The variable nature of β Persei was known to the Arabs who called it Algol, meaning the 'Demon Star,' because of its rapid changes. The Arabs did not know the cause of its fluctuations and indeed it was not until 1782 that J. Goodricke discovered that the light diminished periodically at regular intervals of 2 d. 20 h. 49 m., and he suggested that this phenomenon was due to a companion darker than Algol revolving round it and eclipsing it. It is remarkable that this explanation had been almost forgotten, though it seemed to be the most obvious explanation, until 1889 when H. C. Vogel, using the spectroscope, showed that the spectral lines of Algol were alternately displaced towards the red and the violet in the period of the variation of brightness. Each component is, of course, revolving round the common centre of gravity of the system. Spectral displacements are just what we would expect from a star approaching us at one time in its orbital motion and receding from us at another time, and the same principle has been applied to a large number of other eclipsing binaries. There are many varieties of eclipsing binaries, depending on the relative brightness of the components, their relative sizes, the inclination of the plane of their orbits to the line of sight, the eccentricities of their orbits, and other factors. The study of these stars is a specialized work—like many other departments in astronomy. We have seen how the masses of binaries are determined when their distances and periods of revolution are found, and it is interesting to know that Algol is typical of nearly 400 known eclipsing variables. Fig. 39 shows the principle of eclipsing variables, the darker star being shaded. Much could be said about these stars but we must now consider other types of variables.

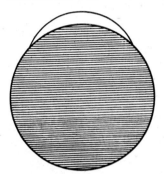

Fig. 39 When two stars are revolving round their common centre of gravity and the plane of their orbit passes close to the earth, each of the stars will pass between the earth and the other star. If one of the stars is a dark body or much darker than the brighter star, an eclipse or a partial eclipse will occur, the brighter star fading for a time. This phenomenon occurs with a number of stars.

Long Period and Irregular Variables

Amongst those stars which vary in luminosity owing to some internal changes are the long-period variables. These are red, giant stars and their periods of variability range from 2 months to 2 years or more, but their greatest frequency is about 300 days. The range of variation is considerable and in extreme cases—like χ Cygni—exceeds eight magnitudes. About

twenty long-period variables are visible to the naked eye, and the best known of these is o Ceti, known as Mira. It varies between magnitudes 3·5 and 9, and though its mean period is 330 days, the interval from maximum to minimum magnitude sometimes varies by as much as a month. We have seen that the long period variables belong to the red giants and some idea of a giant star can be gained from the fact that Mira has a diameter of 260 million miles. It would be possible to place our sun at its centre and Mars at minimum distance from the sun would still lie inside the star ; its diameter fluctuates by as much as 32 million miles. We have seen that stars do not differ much in mass from the sun and this is true of Mira in spite of its enormous size. Its mass is about five times that of the sun and from this it is easily deduced that its average density is 2×10^{-4} that of air at sea level. Its surface temperature is not high—varying from 1800° K. to 2300° K., and so is only about a third of the sun's surface temperature.

Many irregular variables, like long period variables, are red giants but they differ from the latter in certain respects. First of all, they behave in such an erratic manner that it is impossible to predict what they will do. Then the red irregular variables do not alter as much in magnitude as the long period variables, their variations being generally restricted to half a magnitude and in many cases to less than this. There are other irregular variables which are not red stars and their range of variation is many magnitudes. Amongst these are included such well-known stars as *R* Coronae Borealis, *SS* Cygni and *SS* Aurigae, the first of which fluctuates between magnitudes 5.5 and 12.5.

Cepheid Variables

The most important class of variable stars is the short period variety known as the Cepheids. All variables which are periodic and have periods between a few hours and about 50 days, and whose variations are due to physical causes on the stars, not to the effects of other stars eclipsing them, are included in the Cepheid variables. They derive their name from δ Cephei, one of the earliest recognized examples, and they are divided into two classes according to their periods. The *cluster type Cepheids*, or *cluster variables*, have short periods—about 12 hours, and the *typical Cepheids* most frequently have periods of a week.

The typical Cepheids are yellow stars and are super-giants—extraordinarily luminous giants, about a dozen being visible to the naked eye. They are relatively rare. Owing to their great luminosity they are very prominent even in the far-off regions of space. As a rule all the Cepheids show remarkable regularity in their light curves, their increase in brightness being usually more rapid than their decline. The range of light variation is not large—only about a magnitude. The cluster type with short periods are numerous in globular clusters—hence their name—but they are not confined exclusively to clusters and occur in all parts of the sky.

How the Distances of Cepheids are Found

It is remarkable that these stars have been used to determine enormous distances which could not have been found by other methods with any approach to accuracy. In 1912 Miss Henrietta S. Leavitt, of the Harvard

Observatory, was studying plates taken of the Smaller Magellanic Cloud*
and found that there were many Cepheid variable stars in the cloud. She
noticed that the brighter stars required a longer time to go through their
changes in magnitude than the fainter stars, and was able to announce
that a relationship existed between a star's period and its brightness.
Now the stars in the Smaller Magellanic Cloud are so far away from us in
comparison with the size of the cloud that it is possible to treat all the
stars in the cloud as being practically at the same distance from the earth.
In such circumstances the luminosities of Cepheids in the cloud would not
depend on their distances from us but would be due to something inherent
in the stars themselves, masses, temperature, etc., and hence the periods
would also depend upon similar factors. Generalizing for all Cepheids,
whether in the Smaller Magellanic Cloud or not, it is obvious that the
period must depend upon the star's *absolute magnitude*. This will be illustrated from a hypothetical example.

Suppose there are two Cepheids with magnitudes (apparent) m_1 and
m_2 and, to simplify the problem, imagine that their periods are the same.
We have seen that when Miss Leavitt examined the plates she found that
equal periods implied the same brightness for the stars at the same
distance, or in other words, equal periods implied the same absolute
magnitude. When absolute magnitude was fixed for the magnitude of a
star 32·6 light-years distant, this distance was purely arbitrary, and if
two stars have the same absolute magnitude at this distance their absolute
magnitudes would not differ *inter se* if any other distance were selected.
Suppose that the distances of the two stars with apparent magnitudes
m_1 and m_2 are L_1 and L_2 light-years, and that m_a is the absolute magnitude for each star. Then

$$m_a = m_1 + 7·366 - 5 \log L_1$$
$$m_a = m_2 + 7·566 - 5 \log L_2$$

Hence, by subtracting the second equation from the first,

$$m_1 - m_2 = 5(\log L_1 - \log L_2) = 5 \log \frac{L_1}{L_2}$$

Both m_1 and m_2 are determined very accurately by photographic methods
and hence the ratio L_1 to L_2 is known. Suppose for instance that $m_1 - m_2$

is 2·3, then $\log \dfrac{L_1}{L_2} = 0·46$, or $\dfrac{L_1}{L_2} = 2·884$.

This gives the ratio of the distances of two Cepheids but does not
tell us anything about the absolute distance of each one. To apply the
method it is necessary to know the distance of at least one Cepheid
and when this has been found the distances of all the Cepheids can be
obtained when their periods and apparent magnitudes are known. It is
possible to find out in this way how far off many distant nebulæ are,
provided a Cepheid is found in them.

The work of finding the distance of a Cepheid presented many difficulties because the nearest Cepheid is at a distance of about 200 light-years,
and, as we have seen (page 117), trigonometrical methods for finding

* The Magellanic Clouds—the smaller and the larger—are aggregations of stars,
star-clusters and nebulosities. They are not visible in our latitudes, but can be seen
with the naked eye in the southern hemisphere.

parallaxes at this distance are very untrustworthy. Hertzsprung made a determination of the *average* distance of 13 Cepheids in 1913, and from this he deduced the average luminosity of these bodies. Other distances were then derived by comparison of periods. Shapley also carried out a considerable amount of work on Cepheids and concluded that 17·55 must be deducted from the apparent magnitudes of the Cepheids in the Smaller Magellanic Cloud to obtain their absolute magnitudes. In 1929 he modified the figures slightly and adopted 17·78 as the 'zero point.' From the formula for deriving absolute magnitude (page 125), if $m-17\cdot78$ is substituted for m_*, $5 \log L = 25\cdot35$, or $\log L = 5\cdot07$ which implies that the distance of the Smaller Magellanic Cloud is assumed to be more than 10^5 light-years.

Variation Theories

Different theories have been advanced to explain stellar variation but there is still much uncertainty on the subject. On the pulsation theory the star alternately contracts under its own gravitation, and expands owing to the heat produced by contraction. On this theory considerable changes in the diameters of these pulsating stars must take place. Eddington has compiled a table of the theoretical values of such changes for a number of stars and these vary from 10 per cent in the case of ι Carinae to 3 per cent in the case of SZ Tauri. The data are given below and it is interesting to notice how the period of the light variation increases with the luminosity, and also how the radii of the stars increase as well. Reference to methods for finding stellar radii will be made later in the chapter.

Cepheid Variable Stars

Star		Period days	Apparent Visual Mag. Max.	Min.	Absolute Mag.	Radius of Star	Change in Radius %
RR Lyrae	..	0·57	7·1 to	7·8	−0·4	6	4
SZ Tauri	..	3·15	6·5	6·9	−1·6	20	3
δ Cephei	..	5·37	3·6	4·3	−2·2	30	6
η Aquilae	..	7·18	3·7	4·3	−2·6	35	5
Y Ophiuchi	..	17·12	6·2	7·0	−4·0	70	4
ι Carinae	..	35·52	3·6	4·8	−5·1	115	10

The absolute magnitudes have been computed from the mean of the apparent magnitudes. The radius of the sun is taken as the unit in estimating the radii of the stars.

Novæ

There is another type of variable star which differs so much from any of the types previously described that it has been given a special name of its own—Nova or Temporary Star. Stars of this type rise quite suddenly and unexpectedly from obscurity or invisibility, owing to their previous small luminosity, and appear in many cases as bright stars. Their rise to fame is generally short-lived because they sink back again into comparative obscurity in a short time, sometimes in the course of a few months. In 1934 Nova Herculis was discovered by J. P. M. Prentice and it flared up

I

from a very faint star to one of magnitude 2. Photographs of the region of the heavens where it appeared showed that there was a star there of magnitude 15, and hence this star must have increased its luminosity by 160,000-fold in a day or two. From what has been previously said about stellar magnitudes, readers will understand that the above figures are obtained by finding the value of $2 \cdot 512^{13}$, 13 being the change in the magnitude of the star. Taking the logarithm of this we find that $13 \times 0 \cdot 4$ is $5 \cdot 2$, the antilogarithm of which is about 160,000. Such a sudden outburst of light must have been accompanied by an enormous outburst of heat as well, and it seems highly probable that something like an explosion took place. That forces of an explosive character occur in the case of novæ is shown by the fact that the gases surrounding a nova have some-times been seen to expand with a velocity of more than 1,000 miles a second. The phenomenon does not necessarily end with a single explosion ; successive layers are blown off from the surface of the nova at intervals of a few days.

There is a very interesting fact in connection with Nova Persei which was discovered in 1901. A few months after it was discovered a faint glow was photographed around the nova and other photographs taken later showed that this glow was expanding at a rate which was the same as the velocity of light. Of course, the material ejected from the star could not move with such a velocity, and the inference is that the star was within a nebulous matter which was illuminated by the sudden outburst of light produced by the nova. The light was travelling with a speed of about 186,000 miles a second and was illuminating the previously dark nebula which then presented the appearance of an expanding nebula to observers on the earth.

The last bright nova discovered was Nova Puppis. T. Ellis, at Llandudno, was the first in England to discover it, on November 13, 1942. Its magnitude at the time of discovery was 2.

The cause of novæ is not known but there have been several theories to explain them. A collision with another star has been suggested, but as the probability of such a collision taking place is very small, it is impossible to account for all novæ by this theory. It is true that if a collision did take place there would be an enormous amount of heat and light liberated, the kinetic energy of the moving bodies appearing in the form of heat and light. Another theory is that a nova is due to a collision of a star with a nebula, and this is not so improbable as is a collision with another star. There would be a considerable outburst of heat and light in this case, just as there is such an outburst when a small speck moving with high speed strikes the upper regions of our atmosphere. It is much more probable, however, that a nova is due to some outburst within the star itself, but it is not easy to decide on the cause of such a violent outburst. We have seen that some stars pulsate and alter their magnitudes within certain limits, and perhaps a nova differs from such stars merely in degree of fluctuation. It seems likely that the deep interior of a nova is not affected by the sudden release of energy because a nova collapses in a comparatively short time to a faint star, and this would scarcely take place if much of the star had been affected. Hence novæ probably exhibit only superficial disturbances.

Considering the large number of stars which are variable (through causes other than eclipses), it has been suggested that most stars or even all

pass through a nova stage at some time of their existence. If this is so then our sun might become a nova. The inhabitants of the earth or of any other planet belonging to the solar system, if such inhabitants exist, would not be aware of the fact that the sun was a nova, because the whole planetary system would be turned into the gaseous condition almost immediately. Life in every form would be suddenly exterminated and only the inhabitants of some planets of far-off suns would be aware of the fact that a nova had appeared. Astronomers on such distant planets would announce the discovery of yet another nova and perhaps would speculate on the cause of the phenomenon. They would scarcely consider it worth while speculating on the fate of the planets and the inhabitants on them. From the cosmic point of view the destruction of the solar system and the life thereon would be inconsequential.

Stellar Diameters

Reference has been made to the diameters of some of the Cepheids, derived from theoretical considerations. Before describing the principles underlying some of the theoretical methods for finding stellar diameters, a short account will be given of a practical method for determining the diameters of the larger stars, which has been used with great success in comparatively recent times. As this is primarily a work on astronomy it is not proposed dealing with problems in optics, and for this reason certain brief descriptions which follow must be accepted by the reader ; if a fuller account is required he must consult textbooks on optics for various explanations.

When a planet is examined through the telescope it is seen that it has an appreciable disc but this does not apply in the same degree to a far-off object like a star. The better the telescope the smaller a star appears, but even with the largest telescope a star always presents a disc which is brightest at its centre and fades off towards the circumference. This disc, known as the 'diffraction disc,' is surrounded by a number of dark and bright 'diffraction rings,' but, generally, only two of these are visible. If a small telescope is used the angular sizes of the disc and rings are large, and when a powerful telescope is used the disc, while it is smaller, is never so small that it could be called a true image of a star.

Suppose we cover the object glass of a telescope, leaving only two small openings on opposite sides of a diameter of the glass; either of these openings alone will make a star image, though if viewed through the eye-piece it will appear faint. The star image, from what has just been said, is large. If now both openings are uncovered at the same time there are not two images, the image of one being superposed on that of the other. The diffraction disc and the rings remain the same size but the diffraction disc is crossed by light and dark bands which are known as 'interference fringes,' and these dark bands are caused by light paths of unequal length from the two openings meeting and producing interference.

Interference of Light Waves

Interference in sea waves is a well-known phenomenon. If the crest of one wave should happen to coincide with the trough of another wave the effect may be small or nil, one wave cancelling out the other. In

acoustics the same principle operates and many experiments verify it. One of the best known is the phenomenon of *beats*. When two notes which are not quite in unison are sounded together, we have often noticed a palpitating effect, bursts of sound with intervals of comparative silence, then bursts of sound again. These bursts of sound are known as *beats* and are easily explained on the principle of interference. The wave-lengths of the two notes are slightly different though the velocity of propagation of the sound is the same in each case, and hence at some portions of their course the two systems of waves will agree in phase, strengthening each other, while in other parts they will be in opposite phases and destroy each other.

It was known as early as the middle of the seventeenth century that light added to light is capable of producing darkness at given points and in certain circumstances. Fresnel gave a practical demonstration of interference by placing a source of light in front of two mirrors inclined at a very small angle to each other. Owing to this small inclination, the two images of the source are very close together and behave like two sources emitting *coherent radiation*, that is, the difference in phase of the rays was constant over a time-interval sufficiently long to give a definite visual impression. Using monochromatic light—light of one colour—Fresnel produced dark interference bands on a screen placed before the mirrors. At any point on the screen where the distances from the two mirrors differ by an odd multiple of half a wave-length of the light used darkness occurs.

The Interferometer

Suppose the telescope with the two small openings in the object glass is used to look at two stars close together—say a very close binary. The image made by one star will not coincide exactly with the image made by the other, and the two sets of fringes will not coincide. If the stars are far enough apart the bright fringes of one star image will fall upon the dark fringes of the other, the result being an even distribution of light with no visible fringes. The distance between the fringes depends on the wave-length of light and also on the distance between the openings on the object glass. If, therefore, the openings can be adjusted at such a distance apart that the distance from a bright fringe to a dark one is equal to the angular separation of the two star images, all fringes will disappear. The name *interferometer* is given to a telescope like that just described.

On the basis of the laws of light it is possible to deduce the formula that follows, which can be used for two stars ; a different formula is used for a single star.

Let α be the angular distance in radians between the stars (one radian is $\dfrac{180°}{\pi}$ and the number of radians in a small angle is the same as the sine of the angle) so if the reader prefers, let α be the sine of this angular distance. Let D be the distance between the openings on the object glass and λ the average wave-length of the light of the stars. Then

$$\alpha = \tfrac{1}{2}\,\lambda/D$$

The separation of a number of very close stars has been measured in this way.

The same principle is applicable in measuring the angular diameter of a single star, but a small modification is necessary. It has been shown

that a single star gives the same effect that would be given by a double star if its components were 0·41 of the single star's diameter apart, and hence the interferometer measures only 0·41 of the single star's diameter. In the above equation, therefore, it is necessary to multiply α by the factor $1/0·41$, and the formula becomes...

$$\sin \alpha = 1·22 \; \lambda/D$$

As long ago as 1891 Michelson used the stellar interferometer to measure the diameters of Jupiter's satellites, and in 1920 the instrument was employed to measure the diameter of Betelgeuse.

For measuring stellar diameters the separation required to make the fringes disappear generally exceeds 100 inches. Hence the two beams of light coming from a star are separated by a greater distance than can be accomplished by the diameter of the object glass or mirror. For this purpose the effective diameter of the 100-inch reflecting telescope at Mount Wilson was increased to 20 feet by introducing a steel beam 20 feet long placed across the top of the tube of the telescope. This beam carried two pairs of mirrors, the mirrors of each pair being at the same distance from the centre. One pair of mirrors remained fixed and the other pair was adjusted at various distances up to 20 feet apart. The latter received the starlight and reflected it to the two fixed mirrors which in turn reflected it down the telescope tube to the mirror. With a separation of 20 feet, which corresponds to D in the formula, the rings were found to vanish for a few stars. In 1930 another interferometer, having 15-inch mirrors on a 50-foot beam, was installed, which enabled the apparatus to measure smaller stellar diameters.

The application of the instrument for determining stellar diameters will be shown in the following example which gives the actual figures found when the 1920 *beam interferometer* was tested on Betelgeuse.

When the mirrors were separated by 121 inches the fringes were invisible. The mean wave-length was taken as 5750 A, or expressed in cm., 575×10^{-7}. As 121 inches are 307 cm., the formula gives

$$\sin \alpha = 0·000000228, \text{ or } \alpha = 0·047 \text{ second of arc.}$$

Stellar Diameters Deduced from their Angular Diameters

The determination of the star's angular diameter does not supply all the data for finding its diameter in miles. In addition, it is necessary to know its distance in light-years or its parallax. The parallax of Betelgeuse has been measured and found to be 0·017 second, and hence its diameter is found by the rules previously given. A star's distance in miles is $19·2 \times 10^{12}/p$, and hence the distance of Betelgeuse is $1·127 \times 10^{15}$ miles, so its diameter is $1·127 \times 0·047 \times 10^{15}/206,265 = 257$ million miles, or about 300 times the diameter of the sun. Observations of Betelgeuse by Pease conducted over many years show that its diameter varies considerably, and it has been found to fluctuate between 300 and 210 times the sun's diameter.

Stellar Diameters Deduced from Luminosities and Surface Temperatures

Another method for finding the diameters of the stars is based on certain theoretical considerations. When we see a star and estimate its brightness we know that this brightness depends on the distance of the

star and also on its intrinsic luminosity. Allowance can be made for the distance of the star, as we saw in describing how absolute magnitudes are found, and it remains to deal with the factors which are responsible for the star's intrinsic luminosity. As readers may well conjecture, the intrinsic luminosity depends on the size of the star and also on the amount of radiation that it emits per unit of surface—say, each square centimetre. If two stars with the same parallax and therefore at the same distance from the earth have the same intrinsic luminosity it is impossible to decide offhand whether one star is much larger than the other but has a lower surface temperature, and therefore emits less radiation per unit area than the other, the preponderance in size just balancing the less radiation per square centimetre of surface. Obviously if there were any means of estimating the amount of radiation per square centimetre it would then be possible to compare the surfaces of each star and hence their diameters.

Physicists know what the surface temperature of a star is by the radiation laws, as already described on page 30. They can also measure temperatures by the quality of the spectrum, different kinds of spectra corresponding to different temperatures. A blacksmith can make a very good guess at the temperature of a piece of iron which he is heating, by observing its colour, and the physicist can do even better with the analysis of the spectra, because there is no guessing on his part, but a fairly accurate estimate of the temperature of the star's surface. Vega and Sirius show similar spectra and hence we conclude, irrespective of their sizes or distances from us, that their surfaces must be nearly at the same temperature, and in addition, that each star emits the same amount of radiation energy per unit surface. Notice that this does not imply that each star radiates the same amount of energy ; this would happen only if they were the same size. The radiation applies to a unit on each star and hence Vega, the larger star in this case, must radiate more energy than Sirius does.

The intrinsic luminosity tells us how much energy is emitted by the whole surface of the star, and the temperature deduced from the type of spectra tells us how much energy is due to each square centimetre of surface. Dividing the former by the latter we obtain immediately the superficial area of the star, and from this its diameter is found.

The results of these computations are very interesting because they confirm the results deduced from the use of the interferometer. Of course, perfect agreement must not be expected in dealing with problems which involve such minute measurements as are frequently necessary in these cases, but the agreement is as good as can be expected.

A formula has been derived from which the diameter of a star can be computed when its absolute magnitude (page 124) and temperature are known. Without dealing with the method for deriving this formula it will be merely written down and an example worked out from it to illustrate its use.

Let T absolute be the effective temperature of the surface of the star— a temperature derived from a sort of average wave-length which has about the same effect as all the wave-lengths combined. Let m_a be the absolute magnitude of the star and D its diameter expressed in terms of the diameter of the sun as the unit. Then

$$\log D = 5900/T - 0 \cdot 2m_a - 0 \cdot 02$$

Take the case of Aldebaran, whose apparent visual magnitude is 1·06, whose effective surface temperature is 3,300° K, and whose distance is 57 light-years. Using the formula given on page 125, we obtain

$$m_a = 1·06 + 7·566 - 5 \log 57 = -0·15$$

Then, from the above formula,

$$\log D = 1·79 - 0·2 \times -0·15 - 0·02 = 1·80$$

Hence $D = 63$ or the diameter of Aldebaran is about 60 times that of the sun.

This method has been used to determine the diameters of a number of stars which are too small for good results to be obtained by means of the interferometer. The table below shows the parallaxes and diameters of a number of stars, the diameters having been found either by the use of the interferometer or from the formula given above.

Star			Diameters in Terms of Sun's Diameter	Parallax in seconds of arc	Temperature
Antares	..	..	480	0·009	3,100° K.
Aldebaran	..	..	60	0·057	3,300
Arcturus	..	..	30	0·080	4,100
Capella A	..	..	12	0·069	5,500
Vega	..	..	2·4	0·124	11,200
Sirius A.	..	..	1·8	0·371	11,200
Altair	..	..	1·4	0·204	8,500
Procyon	..	..	1·9	0·312	6,600
α Herculis	..	..	400	0·008	2,500
Betelgeuse	..	..	300–210	0·017	2,600
Mira	..	..	300	0·02	2,400

Relation between Stellar Diameters and Temperatures

The table shows that the largest stars, which are red, are also cooler than the smaller stars, and that the sizes of the stars are closely connected with their physical conditions. Blue stars are hotter than red stars, and as we progress along the range of large red stars with decreasing diameters we find that they become less red. There is a limit to this rule because when we come to a certain stage of stellar diameters we do not find the stars becoming bluer and hence hotter, but the spectra now begin to repeat themselves, the small stars becoming redder and cooler. Finally, a stage is reached where these small stars are about as red and also as hot as the red giants, and the name 'red dwarfs' is given to these stars. The smallest of these red dwarfs are about the size of some of the major planets, Jupiter or Saturn. These are not the smallest stars ; smaller still are the 'white dwarfs' which are generally white in colour and whose spectra indicate temperatures close to 10,000° C. or higher. The companion to Sirius is a white dwarf and its diameter is probably less than 30,000 miles. The matter composing this star is so tightly packed that a cubic foot of it would weigh 750 tons. We shall return to the subject of these stars later ; their existence presents many very interesting features to the physicist.

Colour-Index

Readers are probably aware of the fact that the ordinary photographic plate is less sensitive than the eye to red light, but more sensitive to blue and violet light. For this reason red stars are fainter photographically than they are visually, in comparison with blue stars, and this has a very important application in determining stellar temperatures.

If the magnitude of a star is found photographically and also visually and the difference is taken, the relation, photographic magnitude minus the visual magnitude is known as the star's *colour-index*. The photographic is adjusted so that the visual magnitude corresponds with it, on the average, for the type of stars known as the A_0 type, the colour of Sirius, so that Sirius has a magnitude about $-1 \cdot 6$ on either scale. If a star is red enough to be 2 magnitudes dimmer photographically than visually, its colour-index is 2, and so on. Colour-index may be negative in the case of blue stars. Thus, if a star is so blue that its photographic magnitude is $0 \cdot 2$ brighter than visually, its colour-index is $-0 \cdot 2$.

Colour-Index and Stellar Temperatures

An important equation has been deduced from which the temperature of a star can be found when its colour-index is known, and it is interesting to notice that the correspondence between temperatures deduced in this way and those found by other methods is very satisfactory. If T is the absolute temperature of the surface of a star the colour-index of which is I, then

$$T = 7,200°/(I + 0 \cdot 64)$$

If we apply this formula to find the temperatures of Antares, for which the colour-index is $1 \cdot 73$, we find that $T = 7,200/2 \cdot 37 = 3,000°$. Applying it to Sirius for which $I = 0$, we find that $T = 7,200/0 \cdot 64 = 11,200°$. At the most, not more than three significant figures should be used in the final result, because the denominator never contains more than three significant figures.

Classification of Stars

Stars have been divided into a number of classes according to their spectra, and each class has its characteristics, not only with regard to its spectrum, but also with regard to its temperature. The seven principal classes are known by the letters O, B, A, F, G, K, M, and these are subdivided on the decimal system. Thus a star of class G_5 is about half-way between G_0 and K_0 ; B_1 is nearer to B_0 than it is to A_0, and so on.

Stars of class O are blue, having high temperatures and masses. Some of them have temperatures of 50,000° C.,* and their spectra are characterized by ionized helium, doubly and trebly ionized oxygen, nitrogen, etc.

The B class stars are well represented in the constellation of Orion, and their temperatures are about 20,000° C. In these stars, owing to the

---

* When we deal with high temperatures it makes little difference whether we adopt Centigrade or Absolute temperatures because the difference of 273° at a temperature of say 10,000° is very small. In addition, an error of several hundred degrees can very easily occur in estimating the high temperatures that are dealt with in some of the stars.

lower temperature than is found with the O-type, oxygen and nitrogen are only singly ionized. In class A, which are white stars, like Vega and Sirius, the spectral lines of hydrogen reach their greatest strength, and hence the name 'hydrogen stars' is given to them. Their temperature is 10,000° C., and at this comparatively low temperature lines of ionized iron and other metals begin to show.

Class F includes the yellowish white stars whose temperatures are about 7,000° C., and at this temperature metallic atoms in the neutral state begin to give prominent lines. The well-known star Procyon belongs to this class.

Class G includes the sun, and stars in this class have temperatures of about 6,000° C. The star Capella belongs to the G class. Lines of metals in great numbers characterize this class, and the hydrogen lines have weakened in comparison with stars in class F. This weakening continues in the other classes which follow.

In class K the temperature is about 4,000 C., and the lines of the metals now surpass those of hydrogen in strength. These orange stars include Arcturus and Aldebaran.

Class M includes the red stars of temperature 3,000° C. or even lower, and bands of titanium oxide spectrum are present, in addition to the lines. Betelgeuse and Antares belong to this class.

In addition to these seven principal classes, three other classes exist. A few very cool red stars show bands due to carbon compounds, and are known as 'carbon stars.' They are classified as N-type stars, and are the reddest of all known stars. In 1908 Professor Pickering introduced class R, which have weaker carbon bands than class N and are a little hotter. Another class—the S class—is also recognized and is characterized by bands of zirconium oxide, and sometimes of titanium oxide also. Nearly all the stars belong to one of the seven principal classes.

It is interesting to notice that the application of the formula for deriving temperatures from the colour-index gives satisfactory results. Stars of the B_0 class have colour-index -0.33, and the formula gives $T = 7,200/0.31 = 23,000°$ K. The sun belongs to the G_0 class for which the colour index is 0.57, and hence the temperature of stars of this type is $7,200/1.21$, or nearly 6,000° K. It is believed that the formula gives results which are within a 10 per cent error.

If the temperature of a star is found by the above method, its diameter can then be computed by the formula given on page 134, when its absolute magnitude, computed from its parallax, is known.

CHAPTER X

DISTRIBUTION OF THE STARS

THE TWO PRECEDING CHAPTERS HAVE DEALT WITH THE DISTANCES, masses, sizes and temperatures of stars, and a brief outline of some of the methods for determining these was given. The present chapter will be devoted to a consideration of the distribution of the stars in space—a subject on which nothing has yet been said, though many readers may have been anxious to know something about this important side of astronomy.

The Galaxy

If you look at the sky on a clear night when there is no moonlight you will never be able to see more than 3,000 stars above the horizon at any time with the naked eye. The total number that can be seen without optical aid is 6,000 at the most, but, of course, these cannot all be seen at the same time. Atmospheric absorption of light near the horizon reduces the figures somewhat. A broad belt of faint luminous haze which encircles the sky is well known to everyone who has looked at the sky on a clear night, and this is called the Milky Way or Galaxy. The bright stars which are conspicuous to the naked eye are concentrated towards the Milky Way, and in fact all the stars that you can see, and about a hundred thousand million that you are unable to see, belong to this great system. It is remarkable that Democritus, who lived in the fifth century B.C., suggested that the Milky Way was composed of an enormous number of faint stars which could not be detected individually, but it was not till Herschel turned his home-made telescope on this region that the speculation of Democritus was confirmed.

The Milky Way is now known to be bun-shaped, as shown in Fig. 40,

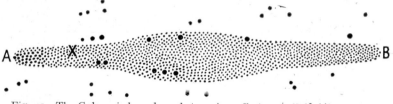

Fig. 40. The Galaxy is bun shaped, tapering off at each end of its greatest diameter. The sun is about 30,000 light-years from the centre of the Galaxy, and is marked X in the figure.

and roughly the 'bun' is six times as long as it is deep, so it is more flattened than most buns and has a certain resemblance to a disc. The greatest length of the Galaxy is more than 120,000 light-years* and its greatest depth about 20,000 light-years. As the figure shows, it tapers off as we recede from the centre, and the sun, marked ×, is not in its thickest part, but is well removed from the centre, and in fact is about 30,000 light-years from the centre of the Galaxy. The stars are strongly concentrated towards the centre of the Galaxy, which lies in the dense star-clouds in Sagittarius, and in other parts they are not distributed evenly. Throughout the Galaxy there are many local star clouds containing numerous stars, and all of these star clouds are far removed from the region of the sun—some of them 30,000 light-years and more. Reference has already been made to the value of the Cepheids in enabling distances to be measured, and, as we shall see, distances very much greater than 30,000 light-years are measured by means of the Cepheids.

The Nebulæ

The word nebula (from the Latin *nebula*, a cloud) has been applied to different objects in the sky which are utterly dissimilar, and unfortunately

* Estimates of the dimensions of the Galaxy differ, and some think that 150,000 light-years may be nearer the greatest length than 120,000 light-years.

non-astronomers are liable to be confused by the term. We shall deal first of all with those nebulæ which are included in the Galaxy, and some of these present a very beautiful appearance with a moderate-sized telescope The Great Nebula in Orion (Fig. 41) is one of the best known of these and is just visible to the naked eye in the middle of the sword of Orion. A small telescope will show that the faint hazy patch visible to the naked eye is very much larger than it was considered to be, and in fact this nebula is about 13 light-years across its greatest length and about 5 light-years across its greatest width. Its distance from us is 600 light-

FIG. 41. THE GREAT NEBULA IN ORION

This great mass of greenish light is one of the most wonderful objects in the heavens. It is just visible to the naked eye in the middle of the sword of Orion.

years—quite a small distance in comparison with that of many other nebulæ. Like other 'white' nebulæ, the Great Nebula in Orion is gaseous, but the gases composing it are extremely attenuated. It has been estimated that the atmosphere in the most perfect vacuum produced by a modern air pump is a million times more dense than the gases in most of the white nebulæ.

Although a first glance at nebulæ through the telescope would lead one to think that they were self-luminous, it is now known that they do not shine by their own light, but shine by the aid of a star or stars embedded in them. The moon shines owing to her surface reflecting the light of the sun, but we must not imagine that the nebulæ shine in the same way by

reflecting the light of a star. The atoms composing a nebula are able to absorb the light from stars of high temperature—the blue stars—and to re-emit it in radiations of different wave-length, and it is this effect which renders the nebula visible. If the star in the gases of a nebula had a low temperature, like some of the giant red stars, they could not stimulate the atoms to re-emit the absorbed light, and we should not be able to see the nebula. A number of dark patches can be seen in different parts of the Galaxy, and those who observe the Galaxy have noticed that it branches into two parts between the constellations of Cygnus and Centaurus, a dark rift intervening. In the southern hemisphere the 'Coal-sack' is very conspicuous and looks like a small cloud concealing the Milky Way which lies behind it. It is now known that these dark clouds, of which there are nearly two hundred catalogued, are really opaque clouds which screen the light of stars behind them, and their opaqueness is due to very fine dust scattered about amongst the gaseous molecules. There is evidence that gaseous matter and fine dust are scattered about in other parts of the Milky Way where neither dark clouds nor nebulæ are seen, and the spectroscope reveals the presence of calcium and sodium in inter-stellar space. The density of this interstellar matter is very small—pro-bably much less than the ten thousand millionth of the density of air when the most perfect vacuum has been produced.

The Globular Clusters

The globular clusters, as their name implies, are globular in shape, each one consisting of thousands of stars which are clustered more densely at the centre than at the periphery. The nearest of these objects are Omega Centauri (see Fig. 42) and 47 Tucanæ, which are about 18,000 light-years distant, and other clusters vary in distances up to nearly 140,000 light-years. As their angular diameters can be measured, and their distances can be determined when Cepheids are found in them, their diameters are easily calculated. These are large, running into several hundred light-years in many cases.

It is remarkable that most of these clusters appear to be in one-half of the sky as if Nature had some special preference for distributing them in an unsymmetrical manner. This distribution is, however, more appar-ent than real. The centre of our Galaxy is also the centre of the globular clusters, but, as we have seen, the sun is not at the centre of the Galaxy, and hence as we look at the clusters they seem to be more numerous in the direction from X to B, looking towards the centre of the Galaxy. A few of the globular clusters are shown in Fig. 40 by the large dots.

Rotation of the Galaxy

The whole system of stars and nebulæ in the Galaxy is rotating round its centre of gravity, but the angular velocity is not the same everywhere. If the Galaxy rotated like a wheel the stars on the outside would have greater linear velocities than those nearer the centre, though all would have the same angular velocity. Instead of speaking of the rotation of the Galaxy it would be more correct to describe each star in the system as revolving round the centre of gravity of the system, just as each planet revolves round the sun in a period which depends on its mean distance

from the central body.   In the neighbourhood of the sun the time of
revolution is 225 million years and the velocity of the stars, comparatively
near the sun, corresponding to the orbital velocity of the planets, is 170
miles a second.   The direction of this orbital motion at present is towards
the constellation of Cygnus.   The sun with all his attendant planets,
satellites, comets, and meteor streams is thus moving round the centre
of the Galaxy with the above speed and in the geological periods has
made about five complete revolutions.   If the solar system passed through
a region of space in which the interstellar matter is relatively dense there

Fig. 42.   The globular cluster ω Centauri is the finest object of its class
in the heavens.

might be some effect on the climatic conditions on the earth.   It has been
suggested that this may have been a contributory factor in producing the
glacial and inter-glacial periods on the earth, but there is necessarily much
of a speculative nature in this view.

The total mass of the Galaxy, including interstellar matter, is about
16×10^{10} times the mass of the sun, and it is believed that the interstellar
matter is responsible for half of this.   The mass of the stars in the Galaxy
is, therefore, 8×10^{10} times the sun's mass, or nearly 10^{11}.   If we assume
that the average mass of the stars in the Galaxy is the same as the sun's
mass, there must be nearly 10^{11} stars in our Galaxy, or about 100,000
million.   The sun itself, as we have seen, occupies an eccentric position

in the Galaxy, and in addition, it is situated in a localized cluster which is probably a star-cloud, like many others to which we have referred earlier. The centre of this cluster lies in the direction of the constellation Carina (not visible in our islands) and its diameter is about 6,000 light-years. The sun is 300 light-years from its centre, and this local cluster, which contains the majority of naked-eye stars and many telescopic stars also, is flattened, just like the Galaxy, its median plane being inclined at an angle of 12° to the galactic equator. The stars in this cluster are all sharing in the motion round the centre of the Galaxy, but in addition, each one has its own motion round the centre of the local cluster. The direction of the sun's motion with reference to this latter centre is not the same as its direction with reference to the centre of the Galaxy, but is towards the edge of the constellation of Hercules, not far from Vega. The sun's velocity in this direction is about 12 miles a second. This was determined by Campbell and Moore at Lick Observatory by using 2,149 stars and measuring the Doppler effect to ascertain their radial velocities, and independent investigations by others confirm their results.

Extra-Galactic Nebulæ

We have spoken about nebulæ which are part of our Galaxy, and now we shall deal with another kind of nebulæ which have nothing in common, so far as physical constitution is concerned, with the gaseous nebulæ. These are known as the spiral nebulæ or extra-galactic nebulæ. Although many of them show no signs of spiral structure this is no valid reason against their spiral form. If the plane of a flattened system lies in or close to our line of sight it is difficult to detect the spiral structure where such exists. On the other hand, if the plane of the system is at right angles to the line of sight, the spiral form, if in existence, is easy to observe. Thus M 51 in Canes Venatici has its plane turned nearly perpendicular to our line of sight and exhibits the spiral form very distinctly (Fig. 43), and if our Galaxy could be similarly viewed from a suitable position, it would probably look like a spiral nebula. The spiral or extra-galactic nebulæ are galaxies just like our own, consisting of thousands of millions of stars. The two extra galactic nebulæ which are nearest to us are M 33 in Triangulum and M 31, known as the Great Nebula in Andromeda (Fig. 44). The latter is about 900,000 light-years distant and is not quite as large as our Galaxy. It can be just seen with the naked eye close to the star ν Andromedæ, of magnitude 4·5, with which, of course, it has no connection, merely lying in the line of sight. The number of extra-galactic nebulæ which can be detected with the 100-inch reflector at Mount Wilson is about two million and it is thought that the 200-inch reflector when it is mounted will be able to penetrate to a distance of 1,000 million light-years, and that about 16 million extra-galactic nebulæ will be within its photographic range.

The Extra-Galactic Nebulæ are running away from One Another

The velocities of the spiral nebulæ are much greater than those of the stars in our Galaxy. Generally speaking, velocities exceeding 100 miles a second are rare among our stars, but many spiral nebulæ are moving with velocities more than a hundred times as great as this. The velocities

of the stars mentioned refer to their individual velocities, not to their orbital velocities round the centre of the Galaxy (see page 141). A nebula in the constellation of Boötes is moving with the enormous velocity of

Fig. 43. The 'whirlpool' nebula in Canes Venatici was the first to show a spiral form in Lord Rosse's great telescope. The star discs which appear on the photograph have no connection with the nebula.

more than 24,000 miles a second, and there must be many others with still greater speeds.

A remarkable fact about these nebulæ is that they are all running away from us and from one another, and the farther they are away the greater is their speed. A nebula 3½ million light-years away has a speed

of about 330 miles a second, and the speed increases in the same ratio as the increase in distance of the nebula, and also decreases in the same ratio as the decrease in distance.   Thus, the Great Nebula in Andromeda,

Fig. 44. The Andromeda Nebula is one of the nearest of the extra-galactic nebulæ, and is less than a million light-years away. The two spiral arms which issue from diametrically opposite points of the nucleus can be seen. Like the other extra-galactic nebulæ, the Andromeda Nebula consists of myriads of stars.

on the above basis, should have a speed of $330 \times 0.9/3.5 = 80$ miles a second, 0.9 representing the distance of the nebula in millions of light-years. The distance of the nebula in Boötes, just referred to, should be

24,000 × 3·5/330 = 250 million light-years, on the same basis. Recession velocities of the spiral nebulæ have been determined by the Doppler effect—the shifting of the spectrum of the nebula towards the red, and the distances of the spiral nebulæ nearest to us have been found by means of Cepheids in them. In the case of the far-off nebulæ it is quite impossible to detect individual stars, and hence no use can be made of the Cepheids in them. The relation between velocity and distance for the closer nebulæ having been established, it has been extended to the far-off nebulæ ; the velocities of recession can be determined by the Doppler effect, and hence their distances can be found. The method is not very accurate and probably a 20 per cent error must be allowed for, but even so, it is a wonderful triumph to be able to find the distances of the far-off nebulæ with such accuracy.

Some disconcerting results have followed the discovery of the recession of the spiral nebulæ. The galaxies are separating to double their original distances in about 1,300 million years, which is only of the order of geological time, and it is a very rude awakening for those who thought of a slow evolutionary process through many thousands of millions of years. When the earth and the other planets were torn out of the sun 3,000 million years ago, as cosmogonists believe, the mutual distances of the galaxies must have been less than one-quarter of their present value, assuming that the recession has been going on at a uniform rate. So many difficulties beset the path of those who hold this view that attempts have been made to explain the Doppler effect on different principles. For instance, it has been suggested that a light-quantum loses some of its energy in travelling from the distant nebulæ to reach us, and for this reason the light becomes slightly reddened. Plausible as this sounds, there are objections to it—the chief of which is that there is nothing in the present theory of light which justifies the assumption of this loss of energy. If we accept the recession of the galaxies as genuine, what light does it throw on the past history of the stellar systems ?

The most probable theory is that originally the separate galaxies formed one great system which, for some reason, exploded, the debris scattering in every direction. Some portions would be shot off with higher speeds than others, and although all the speeds would be modified by the gravitational attraction of the various parts, nevertheless, those shot off with high velocities would retain high velocities (not quite the same as the original velocities), and the same would apply to those with low velocities. Hence at any time each portion would have travelled outwards to a distance which is proportional to the velocity. When we observe the galaxies receding with velocities proportional to their distances apart, these velocities are not due to the distances, but *the distances are due to the velocities*. Of course, the galaxies were not shot off in the form of stars ; the stars condensed from the matter which was expelled, and their method of formation will be considered in the next chapter.

If we accept this view, the stellar systems are not very old, because the matter from which they were formed must have been very close a few thousand million years ago when disruption occurred. On the other hand, there is evidence that the stars are very much older than this. Here is one line of evidence which is difficult to refute.

Of the thousands of millions of stars in our Galaxy we find that they consist of a heterogeneous collection so far as mass and velocity are

K

concerned, velocity referring to each star's individual speed, not to its orbital velocity. Now every star is attracting every other star and although the average distance of one star from another is large, yet in time there is an appreciable effect on the velocities of the stars through their mutual gravitational attraction. The result of this mutual gravitational pull is, on the average, to equalize the energy of motion of the stars, this energy being measured by half the mass of a star multiplied by the square of its velocity. When the stars are grouped according to their mass, and the average velocities of the stars in each group are determined, the average energy for each of the weight-groups is easily found. When this is done it is found that the less massive stars are moving faster, on the average, than the more massive stars, and that the velocities differ approximately by the amount necessary to give the same mean energy for each group. Knowing the masses, speeds, and mean distances between the stars, it is possible to determine the time necessary for this equal partition of the energy to take place, and the computation shows that this time is of the order 10^{13} years. These figures provide, therefore, a lower limit to the age of the stars, and they may have existed longer than this. Other lines of argument point to the same conclusion, and the problem of the recession of the spiral nebulæ still remains without any adequate explanation.

It has been suggested, as a solution of the problem, that the Cosmos pulsates like some of the stars, expanding and contracting, and it is merely by chance that we happen to live during the expansion stage. Perhaps if we had lived during a certain period in the past or if we should live at the relevant period in the future, we might observe that the galaxies would approach one another.

There has been a considerable amount of speculation on this subject, but no useful purpose would be served by dwelling on it. Before leaving the matter, however, reference may be made to an interesting work by Sir Arthur Eddington, *The Expanding Universe*, 1933, and in particular to Chapter IV, 'The Universe and the Atom,' in which a number of very remarkable correlations are developed. Amongst these we may notice that the mass of the proton has been deduced from the velocity of recession of the nebulæ. Incidentally it appears also that the number of protons in the universe is equal to the number of electrons, the number being $1 \cdot 29 \times 10^{79}$. These and other deductions must be considered highly speculative.

CHAPTER XI

STELLAR RADIATION

IN 1870 A PAPER BY J. HOMER LANE APPEARED IN THE *American Journal of Science and Arts*, Series 2, 4, p. 57, under the formidable title, 'On the Theoretical Temperature of the Sun, under the Hypothesis of a Gaseous Mass maintaining its Volume by its Internal Heat, and depending on the Laws of Gases as known to Terrestrial Experiment.' Lane was a pioneer in the investigation of gaseous stars and his work was amplified by others who followed on similar lines to those that he had adopted. It would be interesting to give a summary of the investigations

of a number of physicists, but as many of their results have been considerably modified or discarded, it will be more profitable to deal with more modern research especially in the light of developments in atomic physics.

Boyle's Law

The relation between the pressure p, the density ρ, and the absolute temperature T of a gas is given by the law of Boyle and Charles which applies only to a *perfect gas*. This relation can be expressed as

$$p = R\rho T/\mu$$

where R is a constant and μ is the mean weight of the particles composing the gas, the weight of the hydrogen atom being the unit. Under terrestrial conditions the law does not hold absolutely because gases cease to be perfect gases when compression produces a density exceeding one-tenth that of water. It might be expected *a fortiori* that the law would be very inaccurate for the conditions existing in the interior of a star, but, as will be seen, some remarkable surprises awaited the physicist here.

Lane's Law

Lane reached the conclusion that when a star contracts its temperature continues to rise, provided the material composing the star is so diffuse that it behaves like a perfect gas. As might be expected, the gases in the giants conform to this provision. A curious paradox arose from Lane's law which states that the temperature of a gaseous mass which can be considered to be a perfect gas is inversely proportional to its radius. As a star contracts by radiating heat, the heat generated by the falling in of material towards the centre not only compensates for this loss but also raises the internal temperature. Hence the paradox—the more heat a star loses the hotter it becomes. In Lane's days it was impossible to submit his law to experimental test because there was then no evidence that any stars existed that conformed with the requirements of a perfect gas.

Mass-Luminosity Relation

We shall now refer to the mass luminosity law which was deduced from theoretical considerations and also terrestrial experiments (see Fig. 45). The law was deduced on the basis of a star's interior behaving like a perfect gas, and it was naturally assumed that the red and white giants, which are very diffuse, satisfied the conditions. It was found that the curve fitted in reasonably well with stars whose masses could be found by some of the methods described earlier in this book, and this afforded much satisfaction to those who had been responsible for this important line of research. But then a most disconcerting fact was discovered. It was found that the curve fitted in not only with the diffuse stars but it also fitted in with dense stars as well—those with densities varying from that of water to iron or even much greater. Such an agreement was extremely irritating because such stars should not have fitted in with the theory which was based on the laws of a perfect gas.

There were only two alternatives confronting the physicist. The first of these was to discard or modify the theory, which would have been

very disappointing. The second was to consider the whole question of the conditions in the interior of a star *de novo* and to enquire whether, after all, it would be possible for a perfect gas to exist if it had the density of

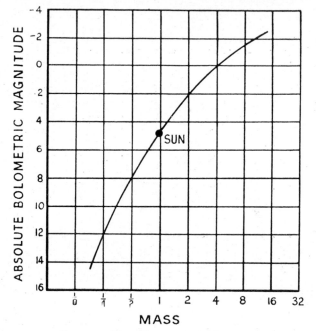

FIG. 45. MASS LUMINOSITY RELATION

Stars of small mass have small light-giving power and those of large mass correspondingly great luminosity. The relation between mass and luminosity is shown in the graph, Fig. 45. The masses of the stars are given with the sun as the unit and the mass of any star can be read off from the graph when its absolute bolometric magnitude is known. Thus a star of absolute magnitude 8 has a mass half that of the sun.

iron, or even much greater. There was a time when no physicist would have seriously entertained the thought of such a possibility, but very often physicists have to be prepared for shocks.

The Interior Matter of Stars is a Perfect Gas

We have seen in Chapter I that the atom is very large in comparison with the size of the electron or proton, and in fact an atom consists mostly of empty space. Under terrestrial conditions it is possible to knock off a few of the outer electrons of an atom, but no temperature in the laboratory is sufficient to disturb the inner rings. When we are dealing with the interior of stars where the temperature may run to many millions of degrees (the temperature of the sun in central regions is about 20 million degrees Centigrade) the atoms are stripped of their electrons which dash about at terrific speeds—up to 10,000 miles a second. It is true that these electrons, like a lot of waifs and strays, are quickly captured by some proton which has lost most of its electrons, but in a very short

interval—a very minute fraction of a second—the annexed electrons are torn away again owing to the high temperature, and so the process of disintegration and annexation is repeated indefinitely. In such conditions it is obvious that there is plenty of room for additional compression before the protons and electrons are jammed together without any space intervening. It has been estimated that jamming will take place when the particles are so compressed that the density of the matter is about 100,000 times that of water. Before this occurs the matter in the interior of a star can be regarded as conforming to Boyle's and Charles' law—that is, we are dealing with a perfect gas—and therefore it is not surprising that the mass luminosity relation should have been found to exist in the dense as well as in the diffuse stars. A remarkable result has been established regarding the nature of the 'perfect gas' in the interior of the denser stars. It appears that it is more easily compressed than an ordinary gas, so that it is not so much an *imperfect* as a *superperfect* gas ! As we shall see later, however, a time comes when the gas is neither imperfect nor superperfect, and then some remarkable consequences ensue.

Assuming that the conditions in stellar interiors are like those just described in the previous section, let us now see what results will follow regarding the output of light and heat.

Waves of longest wave-length are known as the Hertzian waves, which are used in broadcasting, and after these in order of decreasing wave-length there are the infra-red waves, waves of visible light from red to violet, ultra-violet waves, X-rays, Gamma rays emitted by radio-active substances, and finally cosmic rays about which something was said in Chap. I. All these waves are essentially of the same nature as visible light which is restricted to waves of length 8×10^{-5} cm. for red light to waves about half as long for violet light. The 'softest' X-rays, that is, those with the greatest wave-length, extend to about 5×10^{-6} cm., and the 'hardest' X-rays, which have the greatest penetration power, have a wave-length of only 10^{-9} cm. The gamma rays of smallest known wave-length have a wave-length of about 7×10^{-12} cm. Inside a star the X-rays are very numerous and they are very effective in breaking off the electrons from the atoms, which are thus ionized. The fast-moving electrons are able to produce the same effect when they strike the atoms, and thus there is a continuous process of escaping electrons which are captured by ions, only to be knocked off again, and so on indefinitely.

If the result of all this turmoil did not ultimately make its way to the surface of the star we should not know by ocular means that there was such a thing as a star. We should only know of its existence if it came within the neighbourhood of our solar system and disturbed the motions of the planets. It is scarcely necessary, however, to consider this contingency, because if the result of the bustle did not produce certain effects at the surface of the stars, including our sun, it is doubtful if life would exist on the earth or on any other planet.

Radiation Pressure

A very important result of the collisions just mentioned is the pressure exerted by radiation. We have seen that the radiation from the sun has an important effect on the finer particles of the tails of comets, but the radiation pressure in the interior of a star where the temperature is millions

of degrees is very much greater than that of the sun on comets' tails. Some quantitative results will be interesting. It has been shown that at a temperature of 5,000° C. radiation pressure amounts to 0·05 oz. per square foot—a very small pressure but yet capable of being measured— but if the temperature is 20 million degrees Centigrade the radiation pressure is 3 million tons per square inch. (Radiation pressure varies as the fourth power of the absolute temperature.) It might seem that such an enormous pressure acting outwards would disrupt the sun very soon, and this would actually occur if there were not another force holding the sun together—the force of its own gravitation.*

Although the sun or any other star is thus held together in spite of the action of disruptive forces, the radiation (not the individual ions and electrons) gradually makes its way towards the surface of the body. We say 'gradually' because the radiation has not a free passage through the stellar interior. It is continually undergoing the process of capture by the atoms that it encounters and these atoms, retaining the radiation for a minute fraction of a second, re-emit it. In the course of time the radiation slowly fights its way towards the surface of the star, but the continual absorption and radiation lengthen the wave-length until, when it emerges from its prison, it is the mixture of ultra-violet, visual, and infra-red radiation with which we are all conversant. The time required for the radiation to reach the surface of a star depends largely on the mass of the star and may vary from tens of thousands to tens of millions of years. The time is of little consequence because, as the supply is continuously being renewed, once the radiation reaches the surface it will continue in a more or less steady flow.

It has been shown that a star of the radius and mass of the sun would have a temperature of about 20 million degrees at the centre. By the same method it has also been shown that in the case of giant stars with large mass the temperature at the centre is only a few million degrees. The computations regarding the interior temperatures of stars are very much simplified by the remarkable fact that, with the exception of hydrogen it makes little difference what elements we assume in the composition of a star. The explanation of this apparent anomaly is as follows.

The Mean Density of the Particles in the Interior of Stars

Before the physicist can solve some of the problems relating to stellar interiors he must know something about the density of the matter there, or, if he knows nothing about it, he must make some assumptions. Of course, he knows by spectroscopic analysis a lot about the elements found in the atmosphere of a star, but that does not necessarily inform him how these elements are distributed in the interior, or whether all of them are found there. This seems very important when it is necessary to deal with the problem of the support of the upper layers by the gases which exist underneath, but as it happens, it is not really important, because high

---

* Sir Arthur Eddington has pointed out that radiative force, while not prohibiting large stellar masses, makes them risky. It may, for instance, assist a moderate rotation of a star about its axis to break it up, and as a consequence large masses will not often survive. While the force of gravitation collects nebulous material together, the force of radiation pressure chops it off into suitably sized lumps, and this may explain why there is not a very great divergence in stellar masses.

temperatures are great levellers of rank and position amongst the elements. It must be remembered that when the interior of a star consists largely of ions and electrons each of these contributes the same amount of support to the upper layers, irrespective of the elements from which they came. As examples, let us imagine that a star is composed of oxygen the atom of which consists of 8 electrons and the nucleus, or 9 particles altogether. The atomic weight of oxygen is 16 and hence the *average* mass of the particles, if the star consisted of oxygen, would be 16/9 = 1·8. Now suppose the star is composed of sodium, atomic weight 23, and contains 10 electrons and the nucleus, 11 particles altogether. Then the average mass is just over 2. Take platinum, atomic weight 195, consisting of 78 electrons and a nucleus. Dividing 195 by 79 we find that the average mass in this case is 2·5. When the elements are treated in this way the result is always the same—an average of about 2—except in the case of hydrogen. The hydrogen atom consists of a proton and an electron and its atomic weight is 1, so that the average mass of a particle, if a star consisted of hydrogen, is only ½. For this reason the properties of a star will differ considerably according to the proportion of hydrogen it contains.

Proportion of Hydrogen in the Sun

If the diameter of a star and its mass are known it is possible to calculate its absolute magnitude or luminosity, provided the average density of the star is known, and, as we have seen, this can be taken to be 2, unless there is a lot of hydrogen present. Now observation provides us with the luminosity of a star, as explained on page 123, and hence it is possible, by varying the percentage of hydrogen, that is, by assuming a certain proportion of a star to consist of particles of average mass ½, and the remainder to consist of particles of average mass 2, to make the calculated luminosity agree with the observed luminosity. When this is done for the sun it is found that the percentage of hydrogen may be 33 or 99·5. It may seem unfortunate that there are two solutions to the problem and the reason for this is as follows.

Dealing with the majority of stars (white dwarfs are not included) it has been proved that for a given size and mass the luminosity attains a minimum when the star contains 85 per cent of hydrogen. In all cases the proportions refer to mass, not to volume. Suppose a star contains more than 85 per cent of hydrogen ; then the material of the star is less effective in obstructing the radiation, or the 'opacity' of the star decreases, and hence there is a greater outflow of radiation at the surface. When the star contains less than 85 per cent of hydrogen the opacity increases, but the obstruction to the output of radiation causes the temperature to rise and this more than offsets the result of increased opacity, so that the luminosity increases.

It has been pointed out that a 99·5 percentage of hydrogen in the sun is a possibility so far as luminosity is concerned, but as such a high proportion is extremely improbable, the lower percentage—33—has been accepted. It is remarkable that the other stars have been found to contain about the same percentage of hydrogen as the sun, and this fact raises a number of problems.

White Dwarfs

If a star is discovered whose luminosity is less than we expect from the amount of matter that it contains we might suspect that the mass-luminosity law is not always applicable, and our suspicions would be justified. In this connection there is a very interesting story about a certain star which was once considered to be exceptional but which is now known to be typical of many others. The story is as follows.

The bright star Sirius was known for a long time to be moving in an erratic manner, the cause of which was not ascertained until 1844 when Bessel discovered that it was moving in an elliptic orbit. Now a star can only move in an elliptic orbit when there is some object around which it can move, and hence it was recognized that Sirius had an unseen companion, both bodies describing ellipses round their common centre of gravity. Eighteen years after Bessel's discovery the companion of Sirius was seen by Alvan Clark while he was testing his new 18-inch object glass on Sirius. The large modern telescope shows the companion easily, provided it is not too close to Sirius, because in this case it is lost in the glare of the brighter star. We have already shown how the masses of binaries are determined, and when that of the companion was calculated it was found to be 0·8 that of the sun, but it emitted only about 1/360 of the light of the sun. This may seem surprising when we look at the mass luminosity curve, but as the mass-luminosity relation was not known in the early days of the history of this star, its feebleness did not cause much comment as it was assumed to be merely another feeble star just red-hot.

In 1914 Professor W. S. Adams, at the Mount Wilson Observatory, discovered that the companion was not red but white, and the question then arose why it was not shining more brilliantly. A white star should shine more intensely than the sun, which is included among the yellow stars. When its diameter was calculated from its effective temperature and absolute magnitude, it was found to be 30,000 miles. Its mass being known, it was easy to calculate its density, which was found to be about 30,000 times that of water.

For some time it was difficult to explain such an extraordinary density of matter, but ten years later, when the theory of the interior of stars had been developed, it was seen that matter in the stellar interiors might be so compressed that it would have a density far beyond anything that we ever experience under terrestrial conditions. But the companion to Sirius is not unique in possessing such an abnormal density. Soon a few other stars were discovered with similar properties, and in recent times their number has been increased to scores chiefly through the work of Luyten and Kuiper, and it may be presumed that many more await discovery. Throughout the universe there are, therefore, numerous stars in which the electrons and nuclei are jammed so closely together that the material can no longer be considered a perfect gas. The companion to Sirius has a relatively small density if compared with the density of some other white dwarfs. Thus van Maanen's star and some other white dwarfs are estimated to have a density several million times that of water.

Einstein's Theory confirms the Density of White Dwarfs

Einstein's theory has usually been regarded as something which the astronomer is asked to test, as, for example, in the case of the deflection of light by a massive body. Now, however, the theory is used to test certain points which may be considered to be in the category of theory rather than of established fact, and the density of the white dwarfs is one of these. Einstein's theory of gravitation indicates that the lines of the spectrum of a star will be displaced towards the red end of the spectrum, as compared with the corresponding terrestrial lines. The effect is more noticeable in the case of small dense stars because the displacement is proportional to the mass of the star and inversely proportional to its radius. Hence we should expect that the white dwarfs which have small radii would show the effect more than the larger stars. Professor W. S. Adams made measurements of this displacement on the companion of Sirius and found that the shift towards the red end of the spectrum was almost as predicted, an error of only 5 per cent occurring. This may be regarded as another triumph in the realm of science, showing how results obtained in different spheres can be correlated to provide mutual corroborative evidence.

We must now enquire into the origin of the radiation emitted by stars. This will form the subject of the next chapter.

CHAPTER XII

SOURCE OF STELLAR RADIATION

IT WAS POINTED OUT IN CHAPTER II (THE SUN) THAT THE OLD THEORIES advanced to explain the output of the sun's heat were inadequate, and that we must now look to the enormous stores of energy locked up in the atom to account for the energy emitted by the sun and other stars. Knowing the solar constant, it is easy to compute the total energy emitted by the sun in any time, and from this the amount of matter that must be disintegrated to produce this output of energy. In the case of the sun 4 million tons of matter every second are lost, if we assume that the annihilation of matter is the cause of the energy. This may seem very large, but if the sun's radiation were maintained at its present rate the sun would not be completely dissipated before 16×10^{12} years.

Dissipation of Matter proceeds at a Decreasing Rate

The figures given above represent a minimum period for the sun's dissipation, but actually the time would be very much longer than this. The reason is because the more massive a star is the more rapidly it dissipates its mass, and hence, as its mass diminishes, its rate of emission of its substance diminishes too. We can take a homely illustration from the case of a millionaire who is living on his capital alone and who arranges to spend £50,000 a year. At the end of his first year he decides that he must curtail his expenditure as otherwise, if he lives for more than 20 years, he may find himself a pauper. To eke out his capital he decides

to spend four-fifths of his first year's outlay the second year, and in the third year to spend again only four-fifths of his second year's outlay, and so on. His expenditure will therefore be, in thousands of pounds, 50, 40, 32, and so on, and at this rate he need not dread the future. It is just the same with the stars, except that their rate of curtailment differs from that of the millionaire and also that they carry out the policy of economy without conscious effort. The duration of time required for changes of mass is shown in the following table, the mass of the sun being the unit.

Mass of Star		Duration
Very large down to 35		38×10^9 years
35	to 10	65
10	3·7	214
3·7	1·73	930
1·73	0·92	5,210
0·92	0·53	36,300
0·53	0·31	281,000
0·31	0·18	2,190,000

Looking at the figures from 0·92 to 0·53, which may be taken as approximating to the sun, we see that a star a little less massive than the sun would require 36×10^{12} years to become as massive as 0·53 of the sun. To become only 0·18 the mass of the sun this star would require about 25×10^{14} years (obtained by adding the figures in the last three rows).

We have seen that there is some evidence for the existence of the stars for 10^{13} years and hence there is also some evidence for the view that the annihilation of matter is responsible for the radiation from a star. If we shorten the above periods, taking them as about 1 per cent of those given, the results will not agree very well with the large time period previously mentioned. Nevertheless the tendency now is to reject this view of the 'annihilation' of matter as the cause of stellar radiation and to adopt the alternative view that only a small fraction of the energy contained in matter is liberated.

Nuclear Reactions and Stellar Radiation

The reader should refer to Chapter II which anticipated a few of the points to which we shall now return. It was shown that the nucleus of either carbon or nitrogen occurred in the nuclear reactions which generated energy in the sun, the nuclei of these two elements acting like catalysts. The theory was elaborated by Dr. Hans Bethe, though the same thermo-nuclear process for the sun was also proposed by Dr. Carl von Weizäcker. According to this theory the energy production of the sun is not due to the annihilation of matter, but to the transformation of the hydrogen in the interior into helium. The theory was extended to include the 'main sequence' stars about which something will now be said.

Main Sequence Stars

In 1913 Professor H. N. Russell, Director of the Princeton Observatory, constructed a diagram to show the relation between absolute

magnitudes and spectral classes of the stars. This diagram, which is reproduced in Fig. 46, shows that most of the stars are located in a fairly narrow band extending from the upper left to the lower right. The sun,

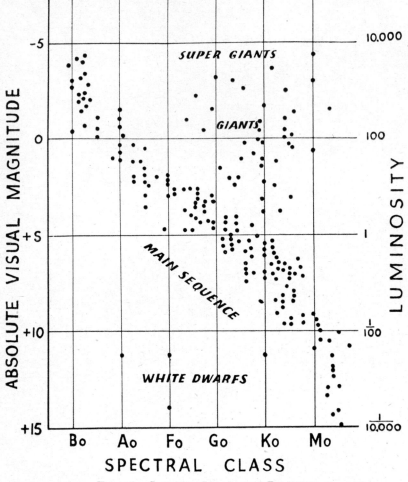

FIG. 46. SPECTRUM-LUMINOSITY DIAGRAM

Absolute visual magnitude is plotted against spectral class for a number of representative stars. Most stars belong to the 'main sequence' which stretches across diagonally from the bottom right to the top left in the diagram. The sun belongs to class Go and has absolute magnitude 4·85. On the right of the diagram luminosities are expressed in terms of the luminosity of the sun as the unit. Super-giants, giants, and white dwarfs do not lie on the main sequence.

a star of the Go class and with absolute magnitude 4·85, is close to the mean curve and occupies a fairly central position along the main sequence. Comparing the sun with the average class A star, it is about a hundred times fainter, and it is about a hundred times brighter than

the average class M star. The stars in this main sequence range from the comparatively cool red dwarfs to very hot luminous blue giants, but it will be seen that there are some stars which lie far away from the main sequence and that these are marked super-giants, giants, and, towards the lower left-hand corner, white dwarfs. Although the absolute magnitudes of the super-giants and giants are small, implying high luminosities, their surface temperatures are low. These two conditions are quite consistent, their high luminosities being easily explicable on the supposition of large dimensions. The high surface temperatures of the white dwarfs, together with their small luminosities, point to the fact that they must be very small bodies. Most of the stars in the main sequence are supposed to emit their radiation from their subatomic energy which is liberated in the process of the transformation of hydrogen into helium, but the same process does not apply to those abnormal stars which lie off the main sequence. In addition, in the case of some of the main sequence stars with small mass, different nuclear reactions take place, and something will now be said on this point.

Thermo-nuclear Reactions in Lighter Stars

Charles Critchfield, an American physicist, was the first to study the reactions which occur in the lighter stars, the reactions taking place between the protons without the catalysing action of other elements. We have already spoken about the deuteron or heavy hydrogen nucleus, page 20, and the reaction which is supposed to take place is as follows :

$_1H^1 + _1H^1 \longrightarrow _1D^2 + e^1$ the protons producing a deuteron and an electron. This is usually followed by the transformation of the deuterium nuclei into the heavier nuclei of helium ;

(1) $_1D^2 + _1H^1 \longrightarrow _2He^3 + $ radiation.

This last reaction, marked (1), begins a new series as will be seen later.

When the temperature of the centre of a star is 15 million degrees the above reaction is as important as is the carbon-nitrogen cycle, and when the temperature is lower than this it becomes of relatively more importance still. It is assumed, therefore, that when we are dealing with light and faint stars in the main sequence the method of energy production is different from what it is in the more brilliant and heavier stars.

Thermo-nuclear Reactions in Red Giants

Some of the red giants have comparatively low central temperatures and none of the nuclear reactions referred to up to the present can take place in their interior. ζ Aurigæ K has a diameter about 160 times that of the sun and a mass 15 times the sun's mass, so its average density is 5×10^{-6}. It is surpassed by ε Aurigæ which is a binary, one of the components, ε Aurigæ 1, having a diameter 2,000 times that of the sun and a mass equal to 25 solar masses. Its mean density is 3×10^{-9}, though the density in central regions is considerably higher than this. It has been estimated that the central temperature of this star is less than a million degrees, and though this may be hot from a terrestrial point of view, it is certain that few nuclear reactions could go on in such conditions.

Some years ago Professor George Gamow, of George Washington University, and Dr. Edward Teller carried out a certain amount of research on the problem of the nuclear reactions in these relatively cool stars, and their results are shown in the scheme which follows.

Starting with the second of the above reactions where deuterium nuclei are transformed into the heavier nuclei of helium, the reactions continue as follows :

(2) $_3Li^6 + _1H^1 \longrightarrow _2He^4 + _2He^3$
(3) $_3Li^7 + _1H^1 \longrightarrow _2He^4 + _2He^4$
(4) $_4Be^9 + _1H^1 \longrightarrow _3Li^6 + _2He^4$
(5) $_5B^{10} + _1H^1 \longrightarrow _6C^{11} + $ radiation
(6) $_5B^{11} + _1H^1 \longrightarrow _2He^4 + _2He^4 + _2He^4$

The reaction between deuterons and protons, No. 1 in the previous series, is extremely rapid and leads to very high energy liberation at a temperature as low as a million degrees.

The reactions for lithium isotopes (2) and (3), that for beryllium (4), and the reaction for the heavier isotope of boron (6), require temperatures between 3 to 7 million degrees. The lighter isotope of boron (5) requires a temperature a little lower than that required by the main sequence stars.

According to Gamow and Teller the coolest red giants, like ε Aurigæ 1, supply their radiation on the deuterium-hydrogen reaction, their lithium, beryllium, and boron supplies being yet untouched. ζ Aurigæ and Capella have exhausted their deuterium supply and are using the elements in (2). Red giants that fall close to the main sequence are deriving their energy from (5) and are preparing to join the normal stars when the light nuclear fuel of boron ends. The different kinds of red giants thus make use of different fuels to supply their radiation energy.

Evolution of a Star

The evolution of a star begins when a giant globe of rarefied and cold gas starts to contract under its own gravitation and as a result, a rise of temperature takes place. When the central temperature approaches a million degrees the first nuclear reaction takes place—the reaction between deuterium and hydrogen. As long as the deuterium supply lasts to keep the reaction going the subatomic energy prevents further contraction, but when the deuterium supply becomes small, contraction starts again. The contraction continues until the central temperature rises sufficiently high to start (2), the thermo-nuclear reaction between hydrogen and lithium, and contraction ceases again owing to the subatomic energy released. The process continues from one stage to another, the central temperature and total luminosity of the star increasing at each stage, until the star approaches the region of the main sequence, where the catalysing action of carbon and nitrogen sets in, as explained in Chapter II. Our sun must have been a red giant in the past and much less luminous than it is now.

The evolutionary courses of stars on the main sequence are similar to one another, and a diagram (Fig. 47) shows the present and future of three stars according to the view of stellar radiation. The bright star

Sirius A (to distinguish it from its companion Sirius B) is near the top and will continue to move more or less along the main sequence until its luminosity has increased by about a hundredfold.   The sun will also move up along the main sequence of stars for about 10^{12} years when it will be as brilliant as Sirius is at the present time.   Krueger 60 B will follow the

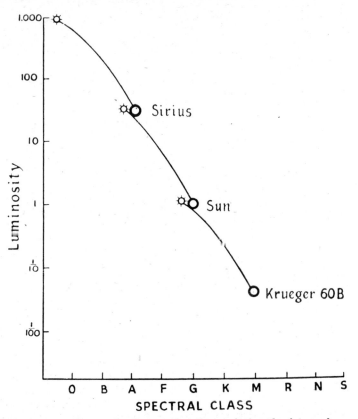

Fig. 47. According to the theory of stellar evolution the future changes in three stars, Krueger 60 B, the Sun and Sirius are shown. The present state of each star in spectral type and luminosity is shown by the symbol ○ and the state after about 10^{10} years by ☼. It will be seen that after the lapse of this period the sun will be about as luminous as Sirius is now and of the same spectral type, while Sirius will have a luminosity 1,000 times that of the sun at present.

same course, in spite of the fact that the nuclear reaction in the interior of this light star differs from that in Sirius and the sun, and in time will be as brilliant as the sun.

It must not be imagined that the stars in the sky will all be brighter in thousands of millions of years, because, while many are increasing in luminosity, others will have exhausted their hydrogen content and will be sinking into old age and obscurity. The stars do not all run through their evolutionary course at the same rate. We have seen that if dissipation of mass were responsible for stellar radiation, the heavier stars would

dissipate their substance away much more rapidly than the lighter stars, and the same applies in nuclear reactions. Suppose that two different stars start at the same time, born out of a nebula, and that they have the same proportions of hydrogen, the more massive of the two will have passed into the old age and senile decay stage while the lighter one is still in the ascending stage. The blue giants in the main sequence have much shorter lives than the lighter stars like our sun and many others.

Most Stars are at the Beginning of their Evolutionary Course

It has been shown in Chapter II that the more rapidly helium is formed the more energy liberated in the reactions is trapped, and in consequence the temperature increases. This increased temperature in turn is responsible for additional nuclear reactions and the temperature of the sun goes on increasing. It has been calculated that the sun will spend about 90 per cent of his life in the first half of his evolutionary track during which the luminosity increases by a factor 10, and only 10 per cent during the remaining half while the luminosity increases from 10 to 100. For this reason there is a greater probability of finding any star at the beginning of its evolutionary course than at the end, assuming that the stars run through the same cycles as the sun. This explains a difficulty which may arise in some minds regarding the mass-luminosity law. If a star can change its luminosity by the factor of 100, why do we not find stars of the same mass but different luminosities, or stars of the same luminosity but with different masses ? The fact that stars spend so much of their lives in the early portion of their evolutionary courses, during which the increase in their luminosities is not relatively large, explains the apparent dilemma. If people remained children for about 90 per cent of their total span we should naturally expect to find that the population was almost entirely composed of children.

Discrepancy in Time Factor

On this view of the cause of stellar radiation, the figures given previously for the time required for stars to annihilate themselves are misleading, the time factor being much too large. Accepting the present view it appears that the sun will use up all his hydrogen in a period of the order 10^{11} years, and then will approach his death and collapse into a white dwarf in a comparatively short time. On the other hand, we have shown reasons for believing that the stars in the Galaxy must be at least 10^{13} years old, and it is difficult to reconcile the two divergent views. This is one of the unsolved problems of astronomy.

Origin of the Stars

We have dealt with the stars and the extra-galactic nebulæ but up to the present nothing has been said about the origin of the stars. While a certain amount of speculation is inevitable in dealing with a problem of this nature, it seems probable that the course of evolution was somewhat on the following lines.

Many thousands of millions of years ago the matter which exists in

the Universe was distributed throughout space as a very diffuse gas with low density. If the density was absolutely uniform there would have been no evolution of stellar systems or stars. It may be assumed that in some parts the density was greater than in others, and as a result there was a tendency for the material to collect in the denser regions. Provided a condensation in any region was sufficiently large it would continue to grow, and it is possible that many condensations were ephemeral, because there is a tendency for condensations to disperse unless they attain certain magnitudes. It is interesting to notice that estimates of the minimum mass of a condensation show that this is of the order of the mass of the spiral nebulæ. It is true that such computations cannot make any claim to extreme accuracy because it is impossible to say what the composition of the diffuse gas was, and a knowledge of this is important in such computations. It may be pointed out, however, that the diffuse nebula could not possibly have condensed into individual stars nor into anything remotely resembling planets ; the condensation must have been on a vastly larger scale—approximating to a mass many millions of times that of the sun.

The next step in the process is to endow each condensation with a rotation, and this need not be considered a mere *ad hoc* hypothesis, because differences of motion in different parts of the primeval nebula would almost certainly initiate rotations, provided the nebula was not homogeneous. We can now focus our attention on one of these rotating nebulous condensations.

Under the force of its own gravitation the nebula would condense, and in doing so would increase its rate of spin. This is a well-known dynamical principle and can be seen in practical application in many ways. The simplest illustration is the case of a child swinging round a vertical pole on the end of a rope which twines itself around the pole. As the rope gets shorter the child moves with increasing speed until it approaches the pole to the utmost limit. The principle is known as the conservation of angular momentum and has a number of important applications in dynamical astronomy. If a body is rotating round an axis and the mass of each small portion is multiplied by its velocity, and that again by its distance from the axis of rotation, the sum for all the small portions composing the body is known as its angular momentum round the axis. It is a well-known principle that this angular momentum must remain constant whatever internal changes may take place in the system, provided that there are no external forces acting. Thus, in the case of the child on the rope, if we consider the weight concentrated at the centre of gravity of the child (not a legitimate assumption in this case, but it is sufficiently accurate for our purpose), and we multiply the weight of the child by its velocity at any instant and that again by the length of rope* then in action, the result is its angular momentum round the vertical pole, and this remains constant. Suppose the rope is 6 feet long when the child is moving with a velocity of 12 feet a second and the weight of the child is 5 stones. Then the angular momentum can be represented by 360, and when the rope is only 3 feet long, as the angular momentum is still represented by 360, the velocity of the child must now be 24 feet a second.

*The length of the rope is used only if the rope is horizontal. As this is never the case it is more accurate to use the horizontal distance of the child from the vertical pole to obtain the angular momentum.

As the child approaches the centre the velocity must increase to preserve the constancy of the angular momentum.

For the same reason the rotating nebula would increase its rate of spin as it contracts on itself and approaches its centre of gravity, and at the same time the system would become slightly flattened like some of the planets (see pages 89, 93). As the speed of rotation increases with additional contraction, a time would arrive when the nebula would assume a lenticular form and then, with still increasing rate of spin, matter would be ejected round the equatorial edge, just as matter would be ejected from the equatorial regions of the earth if it rotated 17 times as fast as it does now. If the nebula were subjected to the gravitational attraction of some of the other nebulæ, as would frequently happen, the matter would not be ejected symmetrically all round the equator, but would be ejected from diametrically opposite points, one point being nearest to and the other farthest off from the disturbing body or nebula. The principle is somewhat similar to the tidal disturbance on the earth by the sun and moon, as we saw in Chapter IV, a tide at a point under the moon and another tide 180° from this point being formed. Systems are known in which matter appears to be streaming from opposite ends of a diameter, thus supporting the above view.

It seems possible that the contracting nebula would break up into a number of condensations and each of these condensations would break up in turn into groups of stars, though small condensations forming directly in the nebula might possibly be able to produce individual stars.

We have traced the evolution of stars from a primeval gaseous matter of low density which broke up into large condensations comparable in mass with the extra-galactic nebulæ. From each condensation local clusters were formed which finally condensed into individual stars comparable in mass with the sun. Nothing has been said about the origin of the primeval gaseous matter, and indeed it is impossible to suggest how it originated. It may have existed always—rather an improbable assumption—but speculation on this question would scarcely be profitable.

Evolution of a Planetary System

After sketching a probable course of stellar evolution it may seem a simple matter to show how the planetary systems originated. Here, however, we are confronted by one of the most difficult problems in the whole realm of celestial mechanics. At first sight it might appear that we only require to advance a few steps in the evolutionary process and to postulate the break up of a star into a planetary system and even to go on further still and to postulate the break-up of a planet or portion of a planet into satellites. Why should a rotating star not throw off planets and why should a rotating planet not throw off satellites ? It seems so simple, but the weapons of mathematical analysis have demolished many beautiful theories regarding planetary evolution. We shall discuss this problem in the next chapter.

Works that can be Consulted

There is a considerable amount of literature on the subject of stellar energy and the interior of stars, much of which appears in various scientific

L

journals which are not easily accessible to the reader. The following books can be consulted for further information.

Sir Arthur S. Eddington, *The Internal Constitution of the Stars ; Stars and Atoms ;* Sir James Jeans, *The Universe Around Us*, especially Chapter V ; George Gamow, *The Birth and Death of the Sun.*

CHAPTER XIII

ORIGIN OF THE PLANETARY SYSTEM

MANY THEORIES HAVE BEEN ADVANCED TO EXPLAIN THE ORIGIN OF THE planets and, generally speaking, these can be divided into two main classes : (1) those which postulate a development of a gradual character ; (2) those which attribute the origin of the planets to a catastrophic source. We shall deal with the first of these, considering the theories advanced by Kant and Laplace.

The Hypothesis of Kant and Laplace

It is not generally known that Kant derived his idea of the origin of the solar system from Thomas Wright of Durham. Wright was primarily concerned with the sidereal system and supposed that the Galaxy was composed of a large number of gravitating systems spread out in a double ring and rotating round an axis perpendicular to its plane. He extended his view, using the solar system as an example of his conjectures, and a year after he had published his work it came to the notice of Kant in 1751. Kant was primarily a philosopher but had very wide interests in other spheres, and Wright's work turned his attention to problems of cosmogony. In 1755 he published his work, *Allgemeine Natur-Geschichte und Theorie des Himmels* ('General History and Theory of the Heavens'), in which, amongst many other matters, he propounded his speculations on the origin of the sun and the planets.

Kant started with a large homogeneous nebula which in time lost its homogeneity on account of the different elements composing it and of their different attractive powers. He believed that the movement of the heavier material towards the centre of the nebula, opposed by gaseous expansion, generated lateral movements, and the whole mass acquired a rotation. Kant was followed by Laplace who held similar views except in one important respect. Instead of assuming that a homogeneous nebula developed its own rotation by means of its gravitational attraction, which actually could not happen because it would violate the principle of the conservation of angular momentum, Laplace simply postulated that it was rotating, without giving the reasons for this rotation. The subsequent developments in the rotating nebula were more or less on similar lines, according to the two theories, and it will suffice to deal with the hypothesis of Laplace.

In 1796 Laplace published his work, *Système du monde*, and pointed out that it was extremely improbable that the orbits of the planets should lie close to a plane, and that the planets should all move in the same direction, if pure chance were responsible. He formulated his nebular

hypothesis, assuming that the original nebula was endowed with a rotation. As a result of radiation from its surface it would shrink, contracting by its own gravitational force when its temperature was insufficient to maintain it in the original diffuse state. In accordance with the principle

FIG. 48. LAPLACE'S NEBULAR HYPOTHESIS

The large ring shows one of the rings supposed to have been left behind as the nebula contracted and increased its angular rate of rotation. Outside this ring a mass of gas is shown condensing into a planet. The central mass is supposed to be contracting further and leaving other rings behind from which more planets are formed.

of the preservation of angular momentum, the angular velocity of the nebula would increase, as pointed out in the previous chapter, and at various stages in its contraction matter would be shed at its equatorial plane in the form of a series of rings. Each of these rings would subsequently condense to form a planet and the matter which condensed would still maintain its original motion when the ring was shed, thus

L*

accounting for the orbital motions of the planets (see Fig. 48). In addition, as the equatorial plane of the rotating nebula would not alter its position very much, if at all, the planes of the planetary orbits should coincide very closely, as we find in most cases. Satellites could have been formed from rotating planets in the same way as the planets were

FIG. 49. THE PLANETESIMAL HYPOTHESIS

This hypothesis, formulated by Moulton and Chamberlin, postulates the approach of a star to our sun thousands of millions of years ago. Great tidal waves were produced on the sun and matter was ejected in the form of two spiral arms. Condensations formed in these and attracted more matter from the material around, forming planets.

formed from a rotating nebula, these smaller bodies being ejected before the matter had condensed into planets in a solid form. A number of phenomena could be mentioned which seem to lend support to the Laplacian hypothesis, but unfortunately for the hypothesis, it is confronted by serious objections.

Objections to the Laplacian Hypothesis

The major objection to the hypothesis is based on the principle of the conservation of angular momentum—a principle which has been respon-

sible for wrecking a number of attractive theories of the origin of the planets. The original nebula had a rotation and therefore, knowing its mass, which would be about that of the sun and all the planets combined, and also its dimensions, which could also be estimated since it must have extended as far as the outermost planet at least, its angular momentum can be found if its velocity is known. Assuming that it extended as far as the orbit of Pluto, its velocity on the periphery must have been about the same as the velocity of Pluto in his orbit, which is known. As the nebula contracted it still maintained its original angular momentum and even when the rings were thrown off, the angular momentum, including that of the rings, would remain the same. To-day, when the nebula has shrunk into the size of the sun and about 1/700 of its mass is concentrated in the planets and satellites, the angular momentum should be just the same as it was when the nebula extended as far as the orbit of Pluto. It is a simple matter to compute the present angular momentum of the solar system, including not only that due to the planets in their orbital motion round the sun, but also that of the sun itself due to its rotation. It is found that the present angular momentum of the solar system is less than 1/200 of its value when the original nebula was rotating. This fact in itself is sufficient to condemn the hypothesis, but there are other objections equally cogent.

The angular momentum of the solar system is distributed in a very remarkable manner. The major planets, whose combined masses are equivalent to about 1/700 of the total mass of the solar system, possess about 98 per cent of the angular momentum, the remainder being nearly all due to the rotation of the sun. How did such a large amount of angular momentum come to be associated with such a relatively small mass? The position of affairs is not what we should expect from a slow process of development, but rather from some catastrophe which tore the planets from the sun, imparting to them a relatively large amount of angular momentum.

Amongst other objections reference may be made to the difficulty of explaining how a contracting nebula could leave a series of rings behind and also of explaining how such rings, assuming that they were formed, could condense into planets. It is much more probable that discrete matter of various masses would be ejected, and that these, far from condensing into planets, would rapidly dissipate into space, their gravitational attraction being insufficient to prevent the dissipative forces. The orbits of the asteroids with their high eccentricities and also fairly large inclinations to the plane of the ecliptic in many cases present a difficulty. Then again, the inclination of the plane of the sun's equator at an angle of about 7° to the plane of the ecliptic is difficult to explain if the earth and the other planets were ejected by a rotating nebula in its equatorial regions. Many other difficulties arise, but it is unnecessary to deal with these, and we shall now proceed to examine some other theories.

Planetesimal Theory of Chamberlin and Moulton

In 1900 Professors T. C. Chamberlin and F. R. Moulton began to develop their theory of the origin of the solar system, and gave the very appropriate title 'Planetesimal Theory' to this new theory. They sup-

posed that the sun a long time ago was emitting eruptions just like erup-
tive prominences to-day, but enormously intensified by the approach of
another star which added tidal effects to the eruptions. As the visiting
star approached closer to the sun a time arrived when two great arms of
matter were ejected, one in the part of the sun directly under the visiting
star, and the other at a point diametrically opposite. This will be better
understood by referring to the action of the sun or moon in producing
tides (page 60–66). The visiting star did not leave the vicinity of the sun
immediately, and so material was ejected at various intervals, which would
tend to follow the direction of the passing star, and as a result two great
arms of matter extended from the sun forming something like a spiral
nebula (Fig. 43). When the star was closest to the sun the matter was
ejected with greater force than when it was farther away, and in the former
case the particles composing the ejected matter moved in very extensive
curves ; in the latter case they travelled along paths fairly close to the
sun (Fig. 49). From the spiral nebula formed in this way, which
must have been incomparably smaller than the spiral nebulæ that we
dealt with in a previous chapter, the planets and satellites were
formed.

The planets were formed by the gradual accretions of the smaller
particles when the star had receded, leaving the matter which was ejected
revolving round the sun in different orbits, a lateral motion having been
imparted to the ejected matter by the star. Cooling of the matter took
place, leading to the formation of small solid bodies and larger nuclei
swept up these smaller bodies, thus forming the planets. The asteroids
arose from masses of material without any very large nuclei, and the
satellites grew up out of small secondary nuclei which accompanied the
planetary nuclei, or they may have been captured by the planets when
they became entangled in the outlying parts of the planetary nuclei. It
will be seen that the theory postulates a gradual building up of planets
and satellites from small particles or planetesimals revolving round the
sun, and hence its title 'Planetesimal Theory.'

Sir James Jeans's Tidal Theory

The Planetesimal Theory may be described as historically the parent
of the Tidal Theory which is due to Sir James Jeans and which was
developed by him in 1916. He did not think that solar eruptions were
necessary and showed that the tidal effects of the visiting star would
in themselves be sufficient to account for the disruption of the sun.
More important than this was his view of the subsequent development of
the planets. Instead of these being formed by the agglomeration of a
large number of small bodies which were cold, Jeans supposed that the
planets were torn from the sun in large masses, that they were once
liquid, and that they received very much less accretions than the Planetesimal Theory demanded. He believed that the primitive sun was not
concentrated like the sun at present, but was very diffuse, extending to
the distance of the outermost planet, but later on he accepted the view
of Dr. H. Jeffreys that the primitive sun at the time of the disruption
was something like the present sun. Two different courses would ensue
from the disruption produced by a passing star according to the state of

the sun. If we are dealing with an incompressible mass of uniform density (an ideal sun which does not actually exist) the disrupted portions would not be of planetary dimensions, but would be comparable in mass with the original sun. If, on the other hand, we are dealing with a body with a strong central condensation—say, a very dense nucleus—surrounded by an atmosphere of practically negligible mass, the disrupted fragments would be small and the mass of the parent star would be reduced very little through the formation of the planets. Obviously our sun must have been like the latter body, since, as we have seen, the mass of all the planets combined is only a small fraction of the sun's mass.

Just as two arms would be formed at antipodal points according to the Planetesimal Theory, so two arms would be formed from the ejected matter according to the Tidal Theory, and these two filaments would condense and form planets. From these planets in turn the satellites would be formed by the tidal action of the passing star or of the sun when the revolving planet passed close to it, or perhaps both bodies would be effective. Filaments emitted from the young planets would give rise to the formation of condensations, and these in turn would give rise to detached masses or perhaps only one mass, thus producing the satellites.

Jeans found it necessary to postulate a close approach of the star to the sun, though he did not think that a collision took place. A great difficulty arose about the rotation of Jupiter, as Dr. Jeffreys showed, and the difficulty could be surmounted only by assuming that the visiting star actually collided with the sun, but not directly. The collision was more a grazing or oblique collision which knocked off some of the sun's surface, the visiting star passing on after the impact. This explained matters a little better than did the theory of a mere close approach, but more serious difficulties arose for which no adequate explanation could be found.

Objections to the Tidal Theory

Assuming, as we must do, that the matter on the surface of the sun was hot, as it is now, the material which formed the planets must also have been hot. Matter which came from the interior of the sun, though the depth would be small, would probably be in a gaseous state in which the molecular velocity would be high—too high for the gravitational pull of the material to control. (See Appendix xii for a mathematical treatment of this point.) The gaseous elements, or at least many of them, would rapidly diffuse into space, and there would be no condensation into planets. Even if we allow that the heavier elements could be retained, and they would have more chance of being retained than the lighter elements, it is difficult to explain the presence of hydrogen on the earth and other planets. It would be very tedious to deal with all the objections to the Tidal Theory, and we shall finally consider the greatest difficulty of all which was pointed out by Professor H. N. Russell in 1935. This objection is based on the angular momentum problem, which, as we have seen, has destroyed a number of beautiful theories.

Professor Russell assumes that the visiting star was the same size and mass as the sun—a reasonable assumption—and that the distance between the centres of the two bodies at the time of closest approach was 976,500 miles, which implies that they were just within the Roche limit

(see page 95), and therefore that their surfaces were about 112,000 miles apart. Tidal eruptions could not have been produced if the distance had been much greater than this. In this case the angular momentum per ton in the case of the visiting star would be 0·25, if that of the earth is 1. Using the same unit of angular momentum, 1 for the earth, all the other planets can be dealt with in a similar way (see Appendix xiii). Taking all the planets, the average angular momentum per ton is more than ten times as great as the angular momentum of the visiting star. If the visiting star had approached the sun closer the discrepancy would have been greater still, and the distance apart has been taken as the most favourable to the Tidal Theory because at a greater distance the tidal effects would not have produced eruption.

How, then, did the encounter with the intruding star impose so much angular momentum on the ejected matter which became the planets afterwards ? Here is a problem requiring some explanation and no explanation has been forthcoming. Incidentally it may be remarked that the above criticism applies also to the Planetesimal Theory. If a grazing collision is assumed the difficulty becomes greater still because the angular momentum of the visiting star would be less in this case, and the factor ten would have to be increased. Within recent years Sir James Jeans, realizing the validity of the objections to the Tidal Theory, has gone back to his early view that at the time when the visiting star approached the sun, our luminary may have been in a diffuse condition, extending beyond the orbit of Pluto. This view, however, seems to raise as many difficulties as it starts out to overcome.

Theory of Dr. R. A. Lyttleton

In 1936 the problem was attacked by Dr. R. A. Lyttleton in an interesting paper which postulated that the sun had once a companion. He assumed that the visiting star ejected this companion and the long filament, which was referred to in Jeans's theory, was developed between the companion to the sun and the intruder. The planets which were formed from the filament were captured by the sun, or at least some of them were, and it was possible that these might all move round the sun in the same direction. Assuming that Pluto is the outermost planet of the solar system (though there is no proof that it is so) the sun's companion would have been about half this distance from the sun. Some support is afforded to the theory from the fact that visual binaries of spectral class similar to that of the sun are about this distance apart. When the primitive planets formed from the filament were condensing, they were in a comparatively small region, and hence their mutual perturbations were considerable. Each planet, when it had moved out of this place, described an elliptic orbit round the sun and returned to the region, and when close approaches between the liquid planets occurred, the satellites were formed.

The method of satellite formation was a weak point in the theory, as Jeffreys showed, and Lyttleton returned to the subject in a later paper and considered the formation of the satellites from a different point of view. Subsequent amendments of the original theory were necessitated by criticism from several quarters and it cannot be said that it has received general acceptance. It may be mentioned that Bhatnagar, a Hindu

astronomer, who has made a very exhaustive examination of tidal theories in general within the last few years, has shown that no existing tidal theory can satisfactorily explain the origin of the solar system.

Professor A. W. Bickerton's Theory of Grazing Collision

Some reference should be made to a theory which was adumbrated before the Planetesimal Theory or the Tidal Theory, but was not very well known in this country. The theory was called the 'Grazing Collision' theory and was due to A. W. Bickerton, a Professor of Physics and Chemistry in Canterbury College, University of New Zealand. Bickerton was not an astronomer, but his interest in the subject was aroused by the appearance of a nova, which he explained by assuming that two bodies had collided obliquely. He applied this 'grazing collision' to explain many celestial phenomena, including the formation of the planetary system. The production of a 'third body,' sheared off from each of the colliding stars, had a prominent place in his theory. His views were published in a New Zealand journal which was not primarily devoted to astronomy, but later they were reproduced in a small work with the title *The Birth of Worlds and Systems*, published in 1911, thirty-three years after he had first propounded his views. The grazing collision of a passing star, according to Bickerton, was the cause of our planetary system, a view which was not taken seriously at the time, but which has been shown quite recently to be not entirely devoid of foundation. Unfortunately he applied his grazing collision theory to so many phenomena that it was largely discredited, even in those spheres where it might be considered an occasional factor. For instance, few will deny that a nova might sometimes occur through a grazing collision between two bodies, but the number of novæ discovered scarcely justifies the theory that they are always due to such collisions.

Some Recent Theories

Within the last few years a number of theories of the origin of the planetary system have been advanced by amateur astronomers who have published their views in *The Journal of the British Astronomical Association*. A very brief outline of these will be given.

In the *Journal*, 52, 6, 1942, July, Mr. J. Miller proposed a theory in which a stellar cluster plays the part of the visiting star in some of the earlier theories. The cluster does not approach the sun but the sun in its motion through space or round the centre of gravity of the Galaxy approaches the cluster. In addition to the sun's gravitational attraction on his outer layers, cohesion of the particles is also a potent factor in delaying disruption through the differential attraction of the cluster. If the cohesion were very small on some of the outer layers, these would not be retained so easily by the sun and would be removed when the cluster was still a long way off. From the debris Pluto was formed, and when the sun approached the cluster closer Neptune was torn off, and so on with the other planets, Mercury being the last to be formed. In this theory cohesion is an important factor in delaying the disruption of the sun's surface.

In the *Journal*, 53, 1, 1942, December, Mr. B. M. Peek attacked the problem from an entirely different point of view. He starts with an extensive nebula, as Laplace did, but does not assign a rotation to the nebula as a whole. Instead of a rotating nebula he thinks that only a small portion of the nebula close to its periphery was in motion, and that this was initiated by random currents. He shows that if the amount of matter in the original random current which was responsible for the motion was ten times the total mass of the planets there would be sufficient material, after allowing for losses by diffusion and other causes, to leave the rim of the partly rotating nebula and form the planets. An original velocity of 2 metres a second in this current—not an extravagant demand —would be sufficient to endow the whole of the incipient solar system with the angular momentum that it possesses to-day. By allowing only a small portion of the original nebula to perform a rotation, much of the difficulty regarding the angular momentum previously mentioned in connection with Laplace's theory is avoided.

The portion in motion near the periphery would gradually communicate its motion to the matter lying deeper in the nebula, owing to viscosity, and when the nebula had contracted sufficiently, particles would begin to leave the edge of the equatorial plane. The manner in which the matter would be ejected is uncertain. It might leave the main mass in a continuous stream or it might become detached as one large mass or even as a single ring, or it might leave it in a succession of discrete aggregations or rings. From these discrete portions the planets were finally evolved, and matter left over from the planetary condensations may have been responsible for the formation of the periodic comets.

The above is only a very brief outline of the theory which tried to avoid, with a certain amount of success, the angular momentum pitfall. In avoiding this danger, however, it is doubtful if it did not introduce greater complications and difficulties than it attempted to overcome.

Lieut.-Colonel K. E. Edgeworth, D.S.O., took up the subject the following year in a paper in the *Journal*, 53, 6, 1943, July, in which he traced the evolutionary history of the stars, planets, satellites and comets from a vast cloud of widely scattered material. For the present purpose it will be sufficient to start with the sun in a condition very similar to its present form, surrounded by a rotating cloud of scattered material extending beyond the orbit of Pluto. This cloud would have the form of a disc, and owing to the reduction of the average random velocities of its particles through random collisions, the disc became thinner. As a result of the disc becoming thinner it became unstable and a number of condensations were formed in the cloud, each of which contracted on itself and became denser, and also developed a rotation on itself. The condensations which were denser than the surrounding medium attracted one another and collisions took place, and in many cases the inelastic condensations coalesced to form larger masses. As a result there was a continual decrease in the number of condensations and a corresponding increase in their individual mass, until finally only one large condensation remained in each particular region. From each of these a planet and its satellites ultimately developed, and the process of development is worked out in a fairly detailed manner. It is also shown how Jupiter was responsible for driving a large proportion of the scattered material in the region now occupied by the asteroids towards the sun, thus reducing its amount, so that

the condensations were small and failed to coalesce into larger ones. The matter simply condensed upon itself and each of these small condensations formed an asteroid. In the outer regions of the cloud of scattered material—far beyond the orbit of Pluto—the condensations were unable to coalesce and condensed on themselves as the material which formed the asteroids, but a very important difference existed between the final result of the condensations. The asteroids developed sufficient cohesion to form solid bodies, whereas the comets remained just as they were from the beginning—a mere agglomeration of loose matter devoid of any cohesion. The different process of development is attributed to the difference in the temperatures of the regions.

Such in brief is the most recent theory of the origin of the planetary system, and like all such theories, it is open to objections.

In the nature of the problem it is inevitable that a considerable amount of speculation should occur in formulating theories of an event which took place at least 3,000 million years ago. Speculation is often necessary in dealing with such matters, but there should be limits to the extent of speculation, especially when it cannot be supported by observational evidence. The present writer has maintained for many years that comets are an insuperable difficulty in every theory so far advanced, and indeed in some cases those who advance certain theories simply ignore comets altogether. The fact that these bodies move in orbits with every inclination and that about half of them have retrograde motion, may not seem very relevant for the origin of the planetary system. It must be remembered, however, as pointed out on page 105, that comets are members of our solar system and that no explanation of the origin of the planets and satellites can be considered satisfactory which does not take account of the comets. Why are so many moving in retrograde orbits while all the planets and asteroids are moving in direct orbits ? If a common origin for all members of the solar system is assumed, this question still awaits an answer.

The recent discovery of two planets outside the solar system will have a profound effect on some of the theories mentioned in this chapter. A planet of about 16 times the mass of Jupiter is now known to be associated with the 61 Cygni system, and another planet more massive still is attached to the star 70 Ophiuchi. Until recently it was believed that planetary systems were extremely rare, because the probability of a visiting star making an approach to another star sufficiently close to cause disruption, was very small. Now it seems that planetary systems may not be so rare as was thought, and this in itself casts a considerable amount of doubt on the tidal theory in any form. Probably in the near future the problem will be solved by an entirely new method of approach.

APPENDIX I

FURTHER REMARKS ON THE ELLIPSE

AN ELLIPSE CAN BE DRAWN BY INSERTING TWO PINS IN A PIECE OF PAPER, passing a loop of string over them, and moving a pencil round the paper, its point keeping the string tight during the process. The pencil point

traces out an ellipse, and each of the points made by the pins is known as the focus of the ellipse (see Fig. 50).

The planets all move in elliptic orbits, but the orbits pursued by most of the comets are considerably more elliptical than those of the planets. In Fig. 51 AB, the line passing through the two foci S and S¹, is known as the major axis of the ellipse, and the line CD which is drawn through

Fig. 50. An ellipse can be drawn by inserting two pins in a piece of paper, passing a loop over them, and then moving a pencil round the paper, the point of the pencil keeping the string tight. The two points made by the pins are the foci of the ellipse. The sun is in one focus of all the planetary orbits and of cometary orbits also. The other focus of these orbits is known as the 'empty focus.'

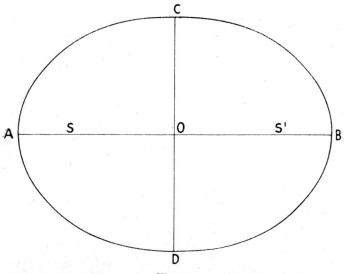

Fig. 51.

the middle point O of AB at right-angles to AB is known as the minor axis. The ratio SO/AO is known as the eccentricity of the ellipse, and the more oval the ellipse is the greater is this ratio. In the case of a circle S, S¹ and O coincide, and the ratio is **0**. When the ratio is large, say, close to 1, the points S and S¹ recede towards A and B, and when the ratio is exactly 1 the curve does not close in again, say, towards B, so a body moving in such a curve, known as a parabola, would go off into space, the sun losing control of it.

APPENDIX II

NOTE ON CENTRIFUGAL FORCE

THE CENTRIFUGAL FORCE OF A BODY MOVING IN A CIRCLE IS MEASURED by mv^2/r, where m is the mass of the body, v its velocity, and r the radius of the circle in which it is moving. If the rotation of the earth were so rapid that in equatorial regions the centrifugal force just neutralized the gravitational attraction of the earth for any mass m, then, since m is common to both the centrifugal force and gravitational pull,

$$v^2/r = g$$

The radius of the earth is approximately 21×10^6 feet and g is about 32, so that $v^2 = gr = 672 \times 10^6$, or $v = 26,000$ ft./sec. very nearly. (see p. 41).

APPENDIX III

ON DETERMINING THE EARTH'S DENSITY

THE EXPERIMENT TO FIND THE EARTH'S DENSITY DETERMINED IN THE first case the earth's mass, but before doing so it was necessary to find the constant of gravitation, an explanation of which follows.

If two bodies are placed at a certain distance from each other their attraction is proportional to the product of their masses and inversely proportional to the square of their distance apart, or, to be more accurate, to the square of the distance between their centres. The attraction is *proportional* to these quantities, but this does not inform us about the absolute attraction between the bodies. Suppose we place two particles each of mass 1 gm. at a distance 1 cm. apart, the attraction between them is $1 \times 1 \times G/1^2$ dynes, where G is a constant, the value of which must be determined by experiment. In the Cavendish experiment it was found that this attractive force was about $6 \cdot 66 \times 10^{-8}$ dynes. Of course, much greater weights and distances than a gram and a centimetre were used, but the reductions were made after the experiment so that the results could be expressed in dynes. In one experiment the two heavy weights were each 348 pounds and the light weights each about $5 \cdot 7$ pounds, and the distance between the centres was $8 \cdot 85$ inches.

The universal constant of gravitation G was found from the experiment to be $6 \cdot 66 \times 10^{-8}$ dynes, and from this the mass of the earth can be deduced as follows :

Let M be the mass of the earth in gms. and r cm. the distance of a

M

particle of mass 1 gm. on its surface from its centre. The attraction is, therefore, GM/r^2, and on substituting 6368×10^5 for r and 6.66×10^{-8} for G, the attraction is easily found to be $M/(611 \times 10^{22})$ dynes. The actual attraction of the earth on a mass of 1 gm. on its surface is 980 dynes, taking 980 as the value of g on the earth's surface. Hence

$$M/(611 \times 10^{22}) = 980, \text{ from which } M = 6 \times 10^{27} \text{ gm. nearly.}$$

The mean density of the earth can be found when its mass is known. The volume of the earth is approximately $\frac{4}{3} \pi r^3$ or 1086×10^{24} cc., and hence its density is $6 \times 10^{27}/1.086 \times 10^{27} = 5.53$.

APPENDIX IV

NOTE ON THE VELOCITY OF ESCAPE

THE ATTRACTIVE FORCE OF A PLANET ON A BODY VARIES AS THE INVERSE square of the distance of the body from the centre of the planet. Let x be the distance of the body at any instant, and let k/x^2 be the force of attraction at this distance. The differential equation of motion is

$$d^2x/dt^2 + k/x^2 = 0$$

The first term in the equation is the acceleration which is g if $x = r$, the radius of the planet. Hence $k/r^2 = g$. Multiplying by $2dx$ and integrating, we obtain the expression

$$(dx/dt)^2 - 2k/x = \text{a constant}$$

Suppose the body starts from rest at an infinite distance from the centre, then, since $dx/dt = 0$ when x is infinite, the constant $= 0$. The equation then reduces to $(dx/dt)^2 = v^2 = 2k/x$

If $x = r$, that is, if we wish to find the velocity of a body starting from rest at an infinite distance when it reaches the surface of a planet, the above equation becomes $v^2 = 2k/r$.

Since $k/r^2 = g$, the final form of the equation is

$$v = \sqrt{2gr}$$

From the above relation it can also be inferred that a body projected from the surface of a planet with the velocity $\sqrt{2gr}$ will go off to an infinite distance, the planet losing control of it.

APPENDIX V

ON FINDING THE PATH OF A METEOR FROM TWO OR MORE OBSERVATIONS

THIS METHOD RESEMBLES THAT USED BY THE SURVEYOR FOR MEASURING distances by using a base line and taking two angles. It is a little complicated owing to the fact that we are working in three dimensions, and

other complications arise from faulty observations, about which something will be said later.

Suppose an observer at O sees a meteor dashing across the heavens and records its position at the beginning and end of its flight, such positions being noticed with reference to some stars. Knowing the right ascension and declination of the stars, he can then say that the meteor moved from a certain right ascension and declination to another right ascension and declination on a certain date at a certain time, and, unless the meteor has a very high speed, he can estimate approximately its time of flight, say 2 or 3 seconds. This latter is not really essential for finding the path of the meteor, but is useful if its speed is to be found. Another observer at O', 20 or 30 miles or even more away from O, also observes the same meteor, and he records its positions too, but, of course, these will be entirely different from those recorded by O.

Astronomers can easily compute the azimuth and altitude for the beginning and end of the paths of the meteor as seen by each observer or, if they have a celestial globe, it is only a matter of a few minutes to set the globe for the latitude of each place and also for the time, and to measure the azimuths and altitudes. Readers are probably conversant with the terms azimuth and altitude, but a few words of explanation may assist some who are doubtful about their meaning.

Draw a great circle through your zenith Z and through a star S, and produce this great circle to meet the horizon at H. The arc measured on the horizon from N, the north, to H, is known as the azimuth of the star. It is reckoned round from N to the south, through the east, and then on until the north is reached again, and hence may be anything from 0° to 360°.

The length of the arc SH is called the altitude of the star and this can never exceed 90°. The complement of the altitude is SZ, and is known as the zenith distance of the star.

A specific example will now be taken to show the method adopted.

Suppose that an observer at Hastings sees a meteor and that the subsequent computation or the use of a globe gives its azimuth and altitude at the beginning of its flight as 310° and 55° respectively. An observer at Maidstone sees the meteor at the same instant and from his observation its azimuth is found to be 273° and its altitude 64°.

Take a map of England and lay one end of a rule on Hastings. With the aid of a protractor lay the rule along an azimuth of 310°. Do the same with Maidstone, so that the rule there runs at an azimuth of 273°. It will be better to draw faint lines on the map which can be subsequently erased without spoiling the map, but the rules will suffice in most cases. Notice that the lines intersect near Epsom, and this shows that the commencement of the flight of the meteor was directly over Epsom. The next step is to find the height of the meteor above the earth at Epsom.

Measuring the distance from Epsom to Hastings we find that it is 49 miles, and also the distance from Epsom to Maidstone is 34 miles. It is obvious that the height of the meteor must be 49 tan 55° or 34 tan 64°, each of which is just under 70 miles, which is, therefore, the height of the meteor when it was first observed.

In a similar manner its position and height are found from the observations at the end of its flight. Suppose that this shows it ended over Chelmsford at a height of 30 miles. The distance from Epsom to Chelms-

ford is 42 miles, and as the meteor had dropped 40 miles $(70 - 30)$ during its flight, the length of its path through the atmosphere is $\sqrt{42^2 + 40^2} = 58$ miles.   If the time of flight is estimated to be 3 seconds, the velocity of the meteor is $58/3 = 19\cdot3$ miles a second.

The computations have been carried out on the assumption that the observers are on a plane, no allowance being made for the curvature of the earth.   This latter has very little effect unless the path of the meteor is very long, and in many cases it can be completely ignored.

The above method shows the principle used, but the actual solution of the problem is not always so simple as it seems.   One great difficulty occurs in the possibility that an observer may miss a portion of the path of the meteor, and when this takes place fictitious results may be obtained for its flight.   In these cases there is always a discrepancy between the heights calculated from each observer's base line, and in many instances this discrepancy is considerable.   For instance, the use of the base line from Epsom to Hastings may give a height of 75 miles, and the Epsom-Maidstone base may give a height of 65 miles.   Of course, the mean of these could be used, but this is a very unsatisfactory way of overcoming the difficulty, because the discrepancy shows that the meteor did not actually commence its flight over Epsom, and a considerable amount of alteration in the positions of its path is required to adjust the differences in the results.

The present writer showed how this trouble could be overcome to a large extent, in *The Journal of the British Astronomical Association*, 46, 8, 1936, June, and this method is now used in this country for computing the real paths of meteors.   Unfortunately the method is too abstruse to be repeated in a popular work of this kind, and readers must be content with the above outline of the main principles involved in the computation of a meteor's path.

APPENDIX VI

NOTE ON THE TIDES

THE FOLLOWING METHOD OF EXPLAINING THE HIGH TIDE ON THE SIDE OF the earth opposite the moon or sun was adopted by the present writer (see *The Journal of the British Astronomical Association*, 52, 8, 1942, September).   Readers may prefer this explanation to some of those usually given in textbooks.   A much fuller explanation, dealing with the tide generating force at any point on the earth's surface, appeared in the *Journal*, November, 1924.   The sun and earth will be dealt with only ; the principle can be extended to the moon or to any bodies revolving round their common centre of gravity.

Let R be the distance between the centres of the sun and the earth, M the mass of the sun, r the radius of the earth, and P a point on the earth's surface directly under the sun, another point Q being at the antipodes with reference to P.

The centrifugal force of a revolving body is denoted by v^2/R, where v is its velocity and R the radius of the circle in which it is moving.   If ω is the angular velocity, then $v = \omega R$, and hence the centrifugal force can be denoted by $\omega^2 R$.   At the point P the distance from the sun is not R but $R-r$, and hence the centrifugal force at P is $\omega^2(R-r)$, assuming that

the earth turns the same face towards the sun, so that the point P is always directly under the sun. Unit mass of a particle at P is assumed.

The sun's attraction on the particle at P is $M/(R-r)^2$, and hence the difference between the centripetal and centrifugal forces is

$$M/(R-r)^2 - \omega^2(R-r)$$

At O, the centre of the earth, the centrifugal and centripetal forces must be equal, otherwise there would be instability and the earth would move away from or closer to the sun. Hence

$$M/R^2 = \omega^2 R, \text{ or } M = \omega^2 R^3$$

Substituting $\omega^2 R^3$ for M in the first of the above equations, the difference between the centripetal and centrifugal forces is

$$\omega^2[R^3/(R-r)^2 - (R-r)]$$

The latter expression can be written in the form

$$\frac{\omega^2}{(R-r)^2}[R^3 - (R-r)^3]$$

Expanding $(R-r)^3$ and $(R-r)^2$, and ignoring all terms containing r/R and higher powers, because r/R is very small in comparison with r, the final result is

Centripetal Force at P — Centrifugal Force at P $= 3\omega^2 r$

Since the term on the right of the equation is necessarily positive, the centripetal force at P exceeds the centrifugal force, and hence the particle at P will have a tendency to move towards the sun. This shows that high tide will take place at a point under the sun.

Now consider the point Q. The centrifugal force on a unit mass at Q is $\omega^2(R+r)$ and the centripetal force is $M/(R+r)^2$; the difference is $\omega^2(R+r) - M/(R-r)^2$. Substituting $\omega^2 R^3$ as in the previous case for M, and reducing, ignoring the squares and higher powers of R, the result is

Centrifugal Force at Q — Centripetal Force at Q $= 3\omega^2 r$

This shows that the centrifugal force at Q exceeds the centripetal force there, and hence the waters of the ocean at Q tend to move away from the earth, thus causing high tide there.

It has been assumed that the earth turns the same face to the sun, to simplify the problem. If the earth's rotation is taken into account this introduces centrifugal forces owing to the axial rotation, and in consequence tides due to such forces would be produced on the earth, the maximum being in equatorial regions. These are super-added to the tides produced by the sun and need not concern us.

The object of the above elementary investigation is to show that high tides on the side of the earth remote from the sun are to be expected, and the same method can be used for the lunar tides also. Quantitative results on the assumption that the earth turns the same face towards the sun differ considerably from the correct results, but these latter can be obtained by endowing the earth with a rotation, as shown in each of the articles referred to. It is unnecessary to introduce this complication in the Appendix, as the object is to show the principle involved in high tide on the side of the earth remote from the sun or moon.

APPENDIX VII

ON THE RECESSION AND APPROACH OF THE MOON

THE ANGULAR MOMENTUM OF A PLANET ROUND THE SUN OR OF A SATELLITE round its primary is obtained by multiplying the mass of the revolving body by its orbital velocity and this again by its distance from the primary. Thus, if m is the mass of the moon and r and v her distance from the earth and her orbital velocity, the angular momentum is mvr. If t denotes the time of the moon's revolution round the earth, then, since her orbital velocity is v, $vt = 2\pi r$, or $v = 2\pi r/t$. Hence the moon's angular momentum is $2\pi m\, r^2/t$, or, since $2\pi m$ is constant, it is proportional to r^2/t, assuming that m, the mass of the moon, remains constant.

Kepler's third law asserts that t^2 varies as r^3, and therefore the moon's angular momentum is proportional to $r^2/r^{\frac{3}{2}}$ or to $r^{\frac{1}{2}}$. Hence if the moon recedes from the earth the angular momentum round the earth increases, and if the moon approaches the earth it decreases.

The total angular momentum of the earth-moon system round the barycentre is made up of the angular momentum of each body, together with the angular momentum caused by the earth's rotation. The principle of the conservation of angular momentum states that this total angular momentum remains constant, whatever changes may take place through internal forces. Hence when the tidal friction produced by the moon slows down the earth's rate of rotation and in consequence the angular momentum of the earth decreases, some compensation must be effected to preserve the original angular momentum the same. This compensation is effected by the moon receding from the earth, her angular momentum, which varies as $r^{\frac{1}{2}}$, increasing. This explains why tidal friction on the earth drives the moon away from the earth, and why she will continue to recede until her time of revolution is the same as that of the earth's rotation, when tidal friction produced by the moon on the earth will cease.

This condition of affairs might continue indefinitely if it were not for the solar tides which will apply a further brake to the earth's rate of rotation, the day becoming longer. Hence a tidal protuberance will be left a little *behind* the moon which will act on it and *hasten* the earth's rotation. This will continue, the angular momentum due to the earth's rotation now increasing, and hence that due to the moon's revolution decreasing. As a consequence of this decrease in the moon's angular momentum, she will approach the earth until the Roche limit is reached, when the earth will disrupt the moon.

APPENDIX VIII

NOTE ON KEPLER'S THIRD LAW

IT HAS BEEN SHOWN ON P. 72 THAT THIS LAW CAN BE APPLIED TO DETERmine the mass of the sun by the introduction of a factor k, expressing the law in the form $a^3 = kT^2$

Take the simplest case of circular motion, which will suffice to show

through which a body would fall in one second ($\frac{1}{2}$ ft², f being the accelera-tion) would therefore be $\frac{1}{2}$ × 0·009 = 0·0045 ft. This shows that the assumption is correct, but, so the story is told, Newton found a discrepancy so great that he could not proceed with his views on gravitation in the universe, and in consequence delayed publishing his *Principia* for nearly twenty years. The discrepancy is supposed to have arisen because Newton made use of an incorrect value of the earth's radius. It is remarkable that he should have used an incorrect value, considering that the dimensions of the earth had been determined fairly accurately at the time he was making his calculations, and also that he should have waited so long before discovering the error.

Mr. J. Miller dealt with this subject in a paper read at the British Astronomical Association in 1939, November (see *Journal of the British Astronomical Association*, 50, 2, 57, 1939, December), and showed that the story of Newton's delay in publishing the *Principia* because of his use of the wrong radius of the earth was apocryphal. Newton must have known Picard's accurate results communicated to the Royal Society in 1672. Miller suggested that Newton had other reasons for the delay in the publication of his famous work.

Although the story of Newton's use of the wrong dimensions of the earth is still repeated and accepted by many, it is now largely discredited, and it is practically certain that the story of his alleged ignorance of the size of the earth is incorrect.

APPENDIX IX

NOTE ON THE RADIATION RECEIVED ON A HEMISPHERE

WE SHALL SIMPLIFY THIS PROBLEM BY CONSIDERING THE AMOUNT OF radiation falling on the semi-circumference of a circle, the radiating object being so far away that the radiation may be assumed to fall on the surface in parallel lines. In the diagram (Fig. 53) let R be the amount of radiation falling on a unit length at P, the radiation being supposed to fall at right angles to this line. If ds denote the length of a small portion of the arc at P, then $ds = r\,d\theta$. Resolving the radiation which falls at right-angles to the line at P at right-angles to the element of the arc, it is seen that this is $R \cos \theta$, and the total amount falling on this element is $R \cos \theta\,ds = Rr \cos \theta\,d\theta$. Hence the total radiation falling on the semicircle is

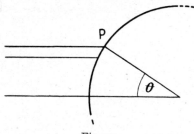

Fig. 53.

$$Rr \int_{-\frac{\pi}{2}}^{\frac{\pi}{2}} \cos \theta\,d\theta = 2Rr.$$

This is the same as the radiation which falls on the diameter of the circle, this diameter being $2r$. The result can be obtained if we imagine

the justification for the above expression. Let a planet describe a circular orbit of radius R in a time T, and let its orbital velocity be v. Imagine that the mass of the planet, which can be taken as a unit, is very small in comparison with that of the sun, whose mass is M. The attraction of the sun on the planet is proportional to M/R^2, and this must be balanced by the centrifugal force of the planet, which is proportional to v^2/R. Hence

$$M/R^2 = v^2/R, \text{ or } v^2 = M/R$$

Since the planet moves through a distance $2\pi R$ in a time T,

$$v = 2\pi R/T$$

Eliminating v between these two equations,

$$MT^2 = 4\pi^2R^3$$

Since $4\pi^2$ is a constant, it follows that

$$R^3 = MT^2 \text{ by a proper choice of units.}$$

When $M = 1$ this gives the relation between the periodic times and distances of the planets, the unit of time being the year and the unit of length the astronomical unit, 93,005,000 miles. If $M = \frac{1}{2}$, the relation is $R^3 = \frac{1}{2}T^2$, etc. It should be noticed that R, the radius of the circle, corresponds to a on page 70, a being the mean distance of a planet from the sun.

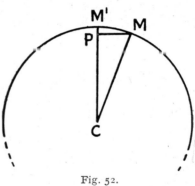

Fig. 52.

In applying the formula to the earth-moon system it was assumed that our satellite is retained in her orbit by the force of gravity, that is, by the same force which acts on bodies at the surface of the earth. There is an interesting story about Sir Isaac Newton in connection with this subject.

Newton, it is stated, attempted to verify this assumption in 1666, and found that there was a discrepancy. His method of approaching the problem will be understood from the following brief outline.

Let M and M′ denote two positions of the moon in her orbit, C being the centre of the earth. Circular motion will be dealt with, the distance of M or M′ from C being R, or 60 times the earth's radius. From M draw MP perpendicular to CM′ and let the angle MCM′ be θ. (Fig. 52.)

Since M′P $= R(1-\cos\theta) = 2R\sin^2\frac{1}{2}\theta$, and M′P is the distance through which the moon falls towards the earth in the time required to move through the arc MM′, it is easy to establish a relation between the earth's gravitational attraction and the moon's motion.

In one second the moon moves through an angle $360°/27\frac{1}{3} \times 24 \times 60^2$, the denominator being the number of seconds in the lunar month, and this reduces to 0·55 second of arc. The sine of half this angle is 0·00000134, and as R, expressed in feet, is 1267×10^6, M′P $= 0·0045$ feet.

The value of the earth's gravitation at a distance of 60 terrestrial radii from its centre is $g/60^2 = 0·009$ ft. sec. per sec., and the distance

that the semicircle is simply projected on the diameter. A sphere is generated by rotating a circle round its diameter, and the above relation which holds for a circle will also hold for a sphere. Projecting a hemisphere on a plane through the centre of the sphere, the area of this projection is obviously πr^2, or the area of a great circle on the surface of the sphere.

APPENDIX X

THE SPECTROSCOPE

THE SIMPLE PRINCIPLES OF THIS INSTRUMENT ARE SHOWN IN THE DIAGRAM. Light from the sun or any other source is admitted through a narrow slit and then passes through a lens or combination of lenses which converts the emerging light into a parallel beam. This beam then falls on the face of a prism, and this splits the light up into its constituent colours. The light rays emerging from the prism then enter the object

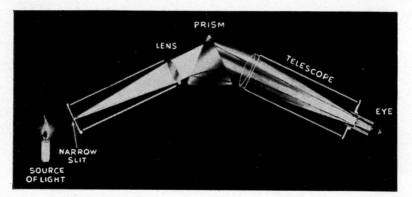

Fig. 54. The principle of the spectroscope. Rays from a source of light pass through a narrow slit and are rendered parallel by means of a convex lens. They then pass through a prism which disperses them into a spectrum which can be focussed upon a plate by a photographic lens, or, as shown in the figure, they can be examined directly by means of a small telescope.

glass of a telescope and are brought to a focus. They can then be viewed with the eye-piece of the telescope or they can be photographed on a plate. (Fig. 54.)

The above is a mere outline and many modifications have been introduced to make the apparatus more effective. Instead of using a prism a diffraction grating is often employed. A highly reflecting bronze made of copper and tin is used for this purpose, and the grating lines are ruled at intervals of about 1/14,000 of an inch. Some idea of the work involved may be gathered from the fact that the ruling machine, run by electric power, must draw the diamond point across the metal nearly 100,000 times to make a 6-inch grating, and the machine must work continuously for about 4 days to complete the ruling.

APPENDIX XI

ABERRATION OF A STAR

IN FIG. 55 OA IS THE DIRECTION OF THE EARTH'S MOTION AND S IS THE position of a star, the displacement due to aberration causing the star to appear at S′. In the triangle SOS′, sin SOS′=SS′ sin SS′O/SO or sin SOS′ = velocity of the earth × sin (earth's way)/velocity of light. The velocity of the earth divided by the velocity of light is tan α, where α

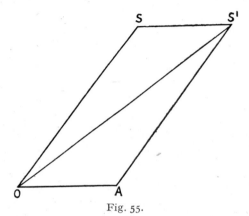

Fig. 55.

is the constant of aberration, or sin α because tan α and sin α can be taken as equal in the case of small angles. Hence it follows that sin aberration = sin constant of aberration × sin earth's way.

As the sines of small angles are proportional to the angles themselves we obtain,

aberration = constant of aberration × sin earth's way.

APPENDIX XII

NOTE ON THE ABILITY OF A GASEOUS MASS TO CONDENSE INTO A PLANET

A GASEOUS MASS TENDS TO SPREAD ITSELF OUT AND TO DISSIPATE ITSELF into space, and unless the original mass exceeds a certain amount, it will be unable to condense into a planet.

The conditions for condensation are

$$m > 9c^3/2^{\frac{5}{2}}\pi^{\frac{1}{2}}G^{\frac{3}{2}}\rho^{\frac{1}{4}}$$

where m is the mass of the nebula, c is the velocity of sound in the gas or gases which compose it, G is the constant of gravitation, and ρ is the density of the gas at the time of ejection. When these constants are substituted the above reduces to the simpler form

$$m > 5c^3\rho^{-\frac{1}{4}} \times 10^{10}$$
$$\text{or } \rho > 25c^6 \times 10^{20}/m^2$$

The value of c cannot be determined exactly because it depends on the nature of the gas and also on the temperature. It can be computed from the formula

$$c = 7650 \sqrt{T/d} \text{ cm./sec.,}$$

where T is the absolute temperature of the gas and d its density when the density of hydrogen is taken as the unit. Thus, if the gas is nitrogen and T is 6,000° K., $c = 158,430$ cm./sec., and $\rho > 395 \times 10^{50}/m^2$.

This last expression can be used to test the different planets.

Take the case of the planet Mercury whose mass is 22×10^{25} gm. Substituting this value in the above expression, it is found that $\rho > 0.8$. In the case of Jupiter whose mass is 19×10^{29} gm., the density must have exceeded 10^{-8}, and taking the earth's mass as 6×10^{27} gm. the density of the ejected gaseous material which condensed to form the earth must have exceeded 10^{-3}. Mars has a mass 6×10^{26} gm., and the density of the material which formed Mars must have exceeded 0.1.

It is very difficult to imagine gaseous material having a density 0.1 and still more difficult to imagine that it could have a density 0.8, which would be necessary in the case of Mercury. In this latter case the ejected material must have been nearly as dense as water. When we deal with the earth and Jupiter and also the other larger planets, it seems possible that condensation might have occurred, but it is fairly certain that Pluto could not have condensed. A temperature about equal to that of the surface of the sun has been assumed, but as most of the material must have come from layers well beneath the surface, the temperature was almost certainly higher than 6,000° K., and this would make the case for the formation of the planets from ejected material more impossible still. If a gas less dense than nitrogen—say hydrogen—is assumed to form the major portion of the ejected material, the possibility of the planets condensing is more remote than the above investigation suggests.

APPENDIX XIII

NOTE ON THE ANGULAR MOMENTUM PER TON OF THE PLANETS

IF v IS THE ORBITAL VELOCITY OF A PLANET AT ANY POINT P, AND d IS THE length of the perpendicular from the focus to the tangent to the ellipse at P, then by an elementary principle in dynamical astronomy, $v = h/d$, where h is equal to $\sqrt{\mu p}$, p being the semi-parameter and μ a constant. The angular momentum per unit mass is vd and therefore is proportional to $\sqrt{p}$. We can assume a ton, or any other convenient weight, to be our unit mass, and find the angular momentum per unit for the different planets. Take the case of the earth, the orbit of which is nearly circular, and assume that its semi-parameter is 1. The angular momentum per unit mass is, therefore, 1. In the case of Pluto whose orbit has an eccentricity 0.248 and whose semi-axis major is 39.46 times that of the earth, the semi-parameter is $39.46 \sqrt{1 - 0.248^2} = 38.22$, and the square root of this is 6.2, which is the angular momentum per unit mass of Pluto. The figures for all the planets can be found in a similar manner.

If the centre of the visiting star made an approach of 0·015 astronomical unit from the centre of the sun, that is, 976,500 miles, the semi-parameter, which is twice the nearest approach of a body in its orbit round the sun, was 0·03 astronomical unit. If x is the ratio of the mass of the star to that of the sun, the angular momentum per unit mass is proportional to $\sqrt{p}\,(1 + x)$, and assuming that the visiting star had the same mass as the sun, this becomes $\sqrt{2} \times 0·03 = 0·25$ approximately.

BIBLIOGRAPHY, ETC.

SOME OF THE FOLLOWING BOOKS WILL PROVE HELPFUL TO READERS WHO WANT fuller explanations than could be given in this volume, or who desire specialised details on certain points raised in the text.

Robert H. Baker, *Astronomy*, D. Van Nostrand Company, Inc., Brooklyn, New York, 1933.

Robert H. Baker, *An Introduction to Astronomy*, 1940.

Charles G. Abbot, *The Sun*, D. Appleton & Co., New York and London, 1911.

Georgia Abetti, *The Sun ; its Phenomena and Physical Features*, Crosby Lockwood & Son, Ltd., London, 1938.

H. Spencer Jones, *Worlds without End*, The English Universities Press, Ltd., 1935

H. Spencer Jones, *Life on Other Worlds*, The English Universities Press, Ltd., 1940.

Russell-Dugan-Stewart, *Astronomy*, 2 Vols., Ginn & Co., New York, Chicago, London, 1926.

R. L. Waterfield, *A Hundred Years of Astronomy*, Duckworth, 1938.

The Harvard Books on Astronomy, edited by Harlow Shapley and Bart J. Bok, published by The Blakiston Company, Philadelphia (London agents, Doubleday Doran) in a number of volumes, deal with specialised subjects in astronomy.

Amateur astronomers will derive considerable benefit from joining the British Astronomical Association. Application should be made to the Assistant Secretary, 303, Bath Road, Hounslow West, Middlesex. Sections under competent Directors are devoted to special branches of astronomy. There is an excellent library with a collection of the best works on astronomy, and the Journal, containing the proceedings of the monthly meetings, is published nine times a year, and keeps members in touch with recent developments. Members pay a subscription of one guinea a year.

A more advanced body is the Royal Astronomical Society, Burlington House, Piccadilly, London, W.1. It was founded in 1822 and is the headquarters of British Astronomy. It is the oldest Astronomical Society in the world.

INDEX